Dancing
Barefoot

Dancing Barefoot

Glyn Brown

Ignite Books
2023

ISBN: 978-0-9932044-9-4

Typeset by Steve at Ignite.
www.ignitebooks.co.uk

Cover design by Alex Vann.
www.alexvanndesign.co.uk

Printed and bound in the UK by
CPI Group (UK) Ltd
Croydon CR0 4YY

Dancing Barefoot

How to be common

An accident-prone memoir
with heroines

Thanks are due all over the place.

Meg Langford and her archives assistant at the Historical Collections & Archives, Oregon Health & Science University; Emma Yandle and Dr Kim Simpson at Chawton House, Hampshire; the Albany Regional Museum, Albany, Oregon; Mack Frost at the Buffalo Bill Center of the West in Cody, Wyoming – all of whom gave permission for images to be used.

The always enthusiastic Mark Riddaway accepted my idea to write about Sally Salisbury for the *Covent Garden Journal*; the idea for this book grew from there. My deepest thanks to Lisa Hitchin, who painstakingly proofread, and to Tim Mapleston for converting ancient images.

Huge thanks to Erica Wagner, whose words mean everything to me; and to Candida Doyle, Kate Mosse and Emma Purshouse for saying amazing things. Thanks also to Tori Amos for her interest in what I've written. Love to Debra Louise Brown for encouragement and warm enthusiasm. All my love to Mavis Brown, my heroine in wellingtons.

Without Steve Pottinger and Ignite Books, I'd still just be sitting on all this information. Thank you for believing in me.

Michael, Flossie, Hildy, Stan and Charles; you are the lights of my life.

Above all, thank you Sally Salisbury, Skittles, Damaris Page, Nell Gwyn, Elsa Lanchester, Aphra Behn, Eliza Haywood, Abigail Scott Duniway, Moll Cutpurse, Memphis Minnie, Suzanne Valadon, Mary Read, Anne Bonny, Esther Pohl Lovejoy, Mabel Stark, Annie Oakley and Raymonde de Laroche. I'm lucky to have you as friends.

This is for Michael, the greatest dancer

1

Girl don't come

Respect yourself. You can do that

They say – or these days secretly think it – you should know your place in life. Well, I never had much grasp on mine. I go for men who know how to pronounce words like Imogen or Goethe, jobs where the only person who sounds like me brings round the post. The gradual accumulation of this coupled with the tragic career slump is probably what caused my mid-point meltdown: years of aiming too high, grabbing stuff I couldn't handle.

Such as? All right, long ago I was a goth, a gauche one. Goths were supposed to read Baudelaire and Rimbaud, so I did that, all very wanton; then, primed, I reached for a bauble way out of my league and fell for a druggy, Baudelaire-quoting, Oxford-educated rock hack. It was like *The Way We Were*, he was a cross between Robert Redford and *Twilight's* Edward Cullen and I was earnest with terrible hair. He had almost every sexually transmitted infection invented. I didn't check, gauchely I thought he'd have said, and I was blinded by the poetry and public school assurance. I'll never grasp the subtext in any environment classier than an Aldi.

Or that's how I used to be.

So that meltdown I mentioned. Eighteen months ago I was sitting at my desk in the middle of it, scratching round for work ideas. I'd done my own stint as a rock writer by then, although as the daughter of a builder and a cleaner I'd been told to get a proper job: checkout or call centre kind of thing, like I ever listen. Now here I was, over-qualified in frown lines and HRT and with a magnificent overdraft.

And a heroine appeared.

'What exactly are you doing?'

Was she talking to me? No, because I'm not Travis Bickle, though the way I was going I could be. Researching a freelance history feature I'd stumbled across a particular woman from the past, and subsequently found several more, who made me sit up. They'd pulled off outrageous achievements, no one knew about most of them, and they had one key thing in common (the word of the day) with me.

We were from awful backgrounds. In our different ways we'd reached for something shiny, the sort of fulfilment people suspected we couldn't really understand. But though we'd been laughed at and discouraged and worse, these women let nothing stop them. They went for their future like gundogs, but what really hooked me is that they found self-belief and a way to be happy, even in sometimes penniless midlife. With much more than I had stacked against them, they cracked it.

I stopped brooding on my car crash existence and looked at them properly. That first one, so explosive she'd practically ripped her way out of the computer screen to stand right next to me. The second hitched herself onto my desk, combing hair into a riding net with her fingers. Discovering the rest took ages, because barefoot females with big ideas rarely got past first post – but at last this rare brigade assembled. I read their stories, of grit and disaster and falling for bastards but still hanging on growling, and realised I couldn't even think about giving up. Though, fighting waves of depression, I'd been on the brink.

One minute. I was seeking inspiration from people who died centuries ago? Apparently. To be honest, they looked a lot more like me than the well-meaning middle-class writers whose self-help books supported each other, drained and exhausted, on my shelves.

Come with me now, back to the start of the show...

✳

Winter, 18 months ago

Another stress-related dream. One of my exes – Craig, the lighting designer who believed in spontaneous human combustion – was offering a twisted sex experience, but he was sitting in an office as he did it, holding up page proofs and grinning. It looked like the supermarket-chain mag I did a subbing stint on, where the plummy editor told me deadlines were so tight, I should *run* to her desk. 'You'll have to sprint over for these first,' said Craig. 'Take in the amends and scamper back like a bunny.' My hind legs were enormous.

I got up after that and thumped down to feed the cats. And by 7.28am I'm at the front door saying goodbye to Steve, my partner. Nothing immediately seems to be wrong with Steve. He doesn't dislike me and he's not solely interested in sex, though I'm sure he wouldn't mind some now and again. What's our central problem? Part of it is coming up in three sentences' time. He pecks me on the cheek and says, 'Get some air today, don't just sit at that computer.' Then he swings his football bag over a shoulder and strides off. Nine years younger than me, in a vintage pinstripe jacket and black jeans, he's mid-forties and looks like a thirty-five-year-old indie rock star. It's not even calculated.

I, on the other hand, look not unlike Hilda Ogden. I'm wearing battered slippers in the shape of tiger feet, a pair of Steve's old pyjama bottoms, a crappy T-shirt from my music writer days and a cardigan fastened with a safety pin. Because I've bleached it for years my hair's a bit dry – actually, it's falling out – so today it's covered with oil like a dangerous tanker spill.

Mumble, 'Yeah. Well, have a good one,' and wave. Then, as he turns the corner and before I can stop myself, jump like

11

Van Halen's David Lee Roth into the street and wave again, quite entertainingly with arms and legs spreadeagled, until I realise the pin's lost its grip and the jumper has fallen open, revealing my unsupported chest through the worn-thin T-shirt. Behind me, a tall, slim girl with a sheet of blonde hair dodges an arm and glances back in disgust. Steve, who'd turned to snap me an air force salute, must've seen that.

Inside, kick the door shut behind me, lean on it with my eyes closed, then shrug, fill my Tigger mug with water and slug back my pink HRT pill. Taking HRT could be the thing that finally does for my once-jaunty breasts. Along with, apparently, nicer hair, optimism, restored sex drive and freedom from hot flushes, HRT sometimes likes to give you breast cancer. It's failed on the rest so this would be typical. My God, my mother died of cancer, how much risk do you want to take? Well... some. I keep hoping the benefits will kick in. And they might've done; perhaps I'd be Jabba the Hutt without it. I suppose I'll have to stop eventually, go cold turkey like John Lennon. (Let's see *him* come off HRT.)

It was standing here by the sink half an hour ago that Steve tried to lighten the mood. When he saw the slippers I heard him softly singing, 'That's neat, that's neat, that's neat, I really love your tiger feet...' As he passed me, I sniffed.

'You wearing aftershave?'

'Dunno.'

I think you know when you're wearing aftershave, particularly if you rarely do. Something's making him happy and it can't be me. I swallowed my anti-depressant. When we met, I'm the one who was full of high jinks. It's *All About Eve*, and I'm Margo Channing. Fasten your seatbelts, gonna be a bumpy ride. Grumpy. Frumpy?

Up in my office, I chuck the aged cat under the chin. A further cat, much younger, stares fixedly out of the window, its twin lying comatose on my chair. So many cats, it's *de trop*.

Observers might say they're child substitutes, and in the case of the "kittens", obtained three years ago, they might be right. Maybe we'll come to why.

Fire up the computer and click on a couple of jobsites. Decades after my heyday on magazines and broadsheets I've turned into a geriatric streetwalker, touting for any dirty job. My current options are a subbing stint in Folkestone, where I will be making a day rate of about £30 once I've paid the train fare; or coming up with features for publications who have so far declined to comment on my ideas. I don't think I can do better, but I'm going to have to try. Otherwise it's back to applying for fruit-packing shifts in Woolwich.

✳

And then, unable to resist, I tap again on the woman I found yesterday. Vivid, bolshy 18th-century courtesan Sally Salisbury, who reached for a life of glittering splendour. A brainy whore who genuinely made good. Until she did something unthinkable.

And yet I want to be her, just because from my first skim-read she lived so big, and let nothing get her down. You'd have to be an inventive and very determined streetwalker to go from squalor to that. Not everyone's Belle du Jour, who was middle class anyway.

Okay. I've got a downpage review for *Mojo*, plus this solitary history-based commission, two hundred pounds for two thousand words (exactly), to finish on Covent Garden's St Giles – in Sally's day a polluted hellhole, the place she grew up and to which she was drawn back. And then I think there's something she can show me. Because would she have ended up – how old was she when she died? *Thirty-three* – on anti-depressants, if she'd been around now?

Of course not. If, as I hope, for the most part she sailed through, what made her resilient enough to keep going in that kind of job, twisting it around to the light, checking for the good things? To give so much that she stood out, in demand by the cultured elite. Where did she get such ambition in the first place?

✳

Walking behind Sally in my mind yesterday I imagined glancing to the side, glimpsing ambitious women like her; wrapped in grimy blankets in the cold and painting, or scribbling in an attic's candlelight. Trying to be something. Versions of me, is how it felt, but in the past, where barriers to stepping out of your lane were higher than sky-high. And I thought, what if there are long-lost left-field moves the most brilliant of these women made that I could customise, mindsets to plunder, random tips? Not just work- but whole life-related. It would be like finding an untouched help and advice site. I wanted to analyse each woman, discover the sort of things Saturday supplements ask Greta Gerwig or Amy Sedaris, understand the emotional highs and lows. There was a juggernaut of experience here. You just had to track it down.

✳

Oh, email! *'Thanks for getting in touch. We don't need feature writers at the moment but I'll keep your details on file...'*

Furiously scribble hard on an old *Standard* until I've gone through several pages. What I might also usefully do, while I'm examining these lives, is chart how I got to the place I'm at, too. A parallel analysis, considering my past with a more positive spin. And see, once I get some momentum, if I can picture a future.

Long ago when I first went freelance, I thought I was a buccaneer rampaging across new frontiers. My skull and crossbones is in holes now, used for years as a cat blanket.

But pirates seek adventure. They spurn a normal life, and never truly lose that fearless spirit because it's part of them.

✳

14

Mrs Sally Salisbury

'Balls.' Hello, it's Sally Salisbury; she's about eighteen. 'Fat. Ugly. Stinking. *Bastard*.' She boots open the door of her room so hard, a panel comes loose. Nearly strangling herself to untie a cape, she punches the wall, briefly checks the mirror.

'Watch the candle! You'll set the place on fire.' One of the other girls strolls in, eating an apple, and several more young ladies installed on the same floor glance over from what they're doing, washing their arms or sewing underwear in the dimness. Sally swipes pins from her heavy hair. 'Smell it. Full of his spunk. He expects me to tease and stroke and shag him, a scrub who has – listen – vomited on himself.' The girl, Polly, say, kicks the core under the bed.

'And the teeth.' She snaps her own together like a whippet. 'Broken tombstones hung with yellow moss.' A very small girl makes a face. 'That's right.' Sally lifts her almost-monobrow. 'Asked me to kiss him on the mouth, that just had spew come out of it.' The child covers an eye. 'You'll have to do this. Going to like it?'

Silence.

'You'll hate it, tiny tramp. But not like I do, because I'm

cleverer than all of them.' Even her biographer, master of smut Captain Charles Walker, is in awe of her mind – 'had she been bless'd with an education proportionable to her own natural genius, she would have been a most accomplish'd woman. And had Sally apply'd herself to that learning, she would have been the Prodigy of the Age'.

Sally fishes a silk purse from her pocket. 'You'll be able to bear it, though, when you get the chinks.' Chink chink. 'Sometimes this, just for an hour. Money it would take you a year to make in a laundry, or if you hadn't been picked for this swanky joint.' She starts to unlace her bodice. 'But I'm aiming for higher things. And a better class of teeth and spew.' Though where she is now, at Mother Wisebourne's above the arches in Covent Garden's piazza, the clientele's teeth are usually not to be sniffed at.

*

Sally was born Sarah Pridden in 1691, probably in Shrewsbury, to bricklayer Richard and his wife Margaret. She had three younger sisters, Peggy, Molly – and Jenny, left blind and disfigured by smallpox, but 'good-natured, very Vertuous' and known for her singing voice. And then you read that Charles Walker's confident Jenny could have gone professional, and certainly had offers from the opera-house – but Sally, wildly jealous, turned them down on her sister's behalf; according to Walker, Sally is a 'little vixen'. Which is not ideal, but no one said she was an angel. Let's give it time.

When Sally is three, Richard is so hard up for work that he moves the family to London's St Giles. It's knee-deep in depravity, and very affordable.

Things start well. Desperate to learn, Sally teaches herself to read (as an adult, she will rip through plays, novels and newspapers, watch tragedies and can write an elegant letter). She also tells people she's planning to live in the West Indies. Keen to nip all this in the bud, her parents apprentice her at

16

nine to a seamstress near Aldgate. Sally is interested in style, so she loves the work and wants to sew for a living.

But then she steals – or more likely loses – a valuable piece of lace and, stunned at her own stupidity, runs away from the job. She's out of work but, knowing she's pretty and having seen beautiful clothes, she picks out the one good item in the house, her mother's petticoat, and hides under the table to take it in so it fits her (she's tall for nine, with fabulous legs). She plans to wear the petticoat to a hopping-ball, a talent show where fancy dancers can win money prizes. But Sally's destined to be repeatedly crushed. Pulling her from the dust and bacon rinds, her dad drags her down to the cellar. He's disciplined this 'wildcat' before, roping her to her bed, locking her in a room for days. Now he strips her (strips her?), ties her to the foot of the stairs, horsewhips her til he's tired and leaves her there, promising to pick up again in the morning.

So much for a mind of your own.

But that *is* what she's got. An artful dodger, she waits. When everyone's asleep she attacks the rope with her teeth, creeps upstairs and is gone into the night. The place that will turn out to be *her* place.

She makes a sort of living shelling peas and beans, then realises she can make a bit more if she gives schoolboys and apprentices half an hour of her time down an alley. Because she's still really a child, and in rags, only the poorer boys go for it; middle-class men don't even see her.

And then they do. When she's twelve, a Dutch merchant goes crazy over her. He buys her lovely clothes – it's *Pretty Woman*, or would be if she wasn't twelve – then proposes. According to Walker, she says, 'Damn you, can I love rotten teeth and stinking fifty?' And leaves. As you would.

Hm. Still, presumably at this point she thinks, I must have magical abilities. She feels a strange power growing, like the wings of a dark angel. What can I make happen next?

Within minutes she's got someone else. At one of her dancing competitions (those legs must be killer), she'd caught the eye of Colonel Francis Charteris. A skirt-chaser, rapist and the inspiration for William Hogarth's nasty and embarrassing *A Rake's Progress*, he's twenty-nine now. Universally despised, this Scottish aristocrat was enchanted by Sally four years ago, and now she's thirteen he's gagging for it. He's got to have her. She wants him, incredibly. He takes her as his mistress.

I mean we saw it coming, but I don't like it either, not one bit. Because you can tell yourself maybe the Dutch guy didn't have sex with her, but now it definitely happens. What was it about all this I found so inspiring, exactly? That I had to actually type the words of her life story? Well, it was that here is the way things were at that time, this is what life would be like if you were poor and female then, and ultimately the story will be how one female triumphed over this crap and made it work for her. Hopefully. Whatever, I'm too invested to stop. I can picture her, kicking a stone along the street, peering into apothecary windows for things to use for make-up. I've got to see this through for her. And what do we have so far? The guy is a violent loser, and it could be the violence Sally goes for, having grown up with it, life's messy that way. But she also has access, genetically or through years of resentment, to a temper that can match Frank's own, an anger that could blow the bloody doors off. Whatever, soon she's sexually experienced, and catapulted into a world of money. Where a flouncy petticoat is, like, nothing.

Back then, taking a child prostitute was licensed paedophilia for men who couldn't handle an adult. Dazzlingly bright, Sally made life fresh for Charteris, chattering away, telling stories like Scheherazade. But by the time she's fourteen he's tired of her. That mysterious power she had depended on subtle elements – among them novelty, doomed to fade – and it would've been easy to plunge back through the cracks. Can't let that happen. This is where her resilience comes in. Guts, fascination about life. Come on, Sally. Show me how it's done.

So she gets a room above a distiller's in New-street (now Covent Garden's twisty New Row). She strolls in her best things, changes her name to Salisbury when someone says she looks like the Countess.

It's still hard. Could she go back to sewing? Long days for little money, and no solid experience. Whereas she's got four years of pleasing men. So she holds people's gaze. Respect yourself. You're a prize and they should beg.

✳

I'm feeling very Mr Angry. This was supposed to cheer me up, but it's winding me up, the way I was driven mad when I read *Lolita*, where I just feel you can't ignore the subject matter, shagging a kid, even if you dig the style. Though I don't like that much either. Does saying this make me look lowbrow? Has the point gone over my head? Humbert Humbert's a literature professor, while Lolita, twelve at the start, and her mum are trailer trash. What if Humbert flipped burgers, would it still be lovely?

But. Is that Sally's life? No, actually. It's her decision to do what she does. It's business, and she requires payment. Probably it's lucky men want to sleep with nymphets, or she might starve.

Of course, the fact that most other trades aren't open to her is a male decision in the first place.

✳

At seventeen, she effectively gets an agent.

Elizabeth Wisebourne had lived in Italy, where she saw the elegant way seraglios – Italian for high-class knocking shops – operated. In London, she arranged meetings with elite courtesans and was soon running an upscale brothel in Drury Lane. She spots our girl, takes her home, spins her

19

round naked ('hm, nice legs'), and starts turning her into a polished woman of the town. Bingo.

This is roughly where we barged in on Sally having a strop, but soon she gets better clients and becomes their favourite. Stunning now and very droll, she's got genuine clout. And for Wisebourne it's a coup, like having Cara Delevingne or Gisele Bündchen signed to your books. The chance to see her brings sophisticated men to the yard, they're happy just to be in the building.

✳

'It was better, yes. This was what I wanted. Not adoration. *Conversation.* Men talking to me like I was human.' There's a reek of sweat in my room, a rustle of taffeta. Would she speak like this, if she was here, and it feels like she is? Slightly sarcastic, but with emotion underneath. Possibly. My dream companion, a Georgian-era Amy Winehouse.

Did they really want to know what you thought?

'They said they did. And they replied, so they must've heard me. If they didn't respond adequately I was a bit of a bitch, ran linguistic rings round them then confused them with my gutter patter. Except they weren't taking me seriously, even the intellectual noblemen, leaning forward, chin in hand. Especially them. Fool, I didn't realise at the start.'

No.

'Because whatever I said, I still sounded like I do.'

Yes.

She flumps into my broken rattan chair. 'But some of them were beautiful, you know? Gene pools you wouldn't believe.' She bites a fingernail. 'And some... almost cared. Champagne. Have you had that? And food I didn't know how to eat, using utensils I'd never seen.'

Like origami, I find.

'Exquisite garments bought for me, earrings, necklaces. And carriages. But most of all, the discourse, the stimulation.'

A sigh. 'I was off my head.'

She turns to me.

'Can I just ask, are these clothes your own choice?'

I glance down.

This is my weekday gear. My 'concentrating on work' gear.

'And that work is... farm work?'

Very, very funny. That's definitely what someone who dresses nicely, for their job or because they feel they're worth it, would think.

✳

So surely here's where common sense comes in? Free-thinking politician Lord Bolingbroke says he's mad about her, so is the Duke of Richmond. Isn't this the moment to lay down the perfect hand and sweep up a comfortable future?

But she can't do it. Warped by everything that's happened, she's too volatile to win over a grandee and be a long-term mistress – or wife, though that's rare for whores. And she *is* quicker than most of the men, and the contempt makes her take risks. She's out with poet Matthew Prior, who treats her as a muse, and starts secretly snipping off bits of his wig. Because she's twenty and a star, this is a laugh, the wacky Cara Delevingne celeb behaviour she's famous for. Except it makes Prior look stupid.

And then at twenty-three she gets pregnant. That's despite the contraceptive lump of sheep's wool or sponge soaked in vinegar and the hot-water douches. Wisebourne sorts out an abortion. Fairly soon after, Sally gets a sexually transmitted disease – probably syphilis – and Wisebourne has a tame physician treat her, though it takes five weeks before she's clear.

If she really is.

And these two moments mark a change. She'd probably known she was going to get disease after disease; but then the big ones kick in. As for the abortion, which you'd think someone like Sally, who attached herself to no one, might sail

21

through – it upset her so much, she kept the embryo preserved in her room. Who *keeps* an embryo? Perhaps someone who knows the baby might have loved them, with a simple love you needn't perform for.

✳

We're watching a slow motion train wreck. So something did get to Sally, past the defences and right to her fine mind and sensitive heart. If every baby has to be got rid of, because Wisebourne's not running a crèche, what is she working for? The money, most of which goes to Wisebourne? The good times? Come on, honey, get that corset on, your next punter's here. Something in her, the last of her naivety, crumples. She's reborn as The Terminator but with screws loose. She puts away booze like there's no tomorrow: 'Usquebaugh Tea' – tea with a big slug of whisky – and barrels of *ratafia*, a liqueur so strong it could strip paint off the hulls of ships.

There's an edgy, Joker-style draw to her escalating behaviour; the sort of pull that attracted men, in the 1980s, to the mad psychodramas of *Betty Blue*. Lord Orr makes her an allowance of 8000 crowns a year to live in the style she now requires. A minor royal, enchanted when, on a booze-ridden night out, she reaches for his sword and holds it to another man's chest, threatening to plunge it in if he won't drain his glass (he drains it) pledges her even more money. She briefly has an impressive house taken for her, possibly near the Inns of Court behind Fleet Street. But that goes wrong, because either she upsets her benefactor, or she doesn't like being alone. And yet here's something touching. Around this time, she tells a nobleman she's developing unexpected feelings for that she's caught a baby goldfinch and is feeding it by hand. Because of who he is, he'd probably be moved by that side of her, a softness no one else sees.

Partly, the frantic theatrics must be a neurotic effort to get noticed by the newssheets; as younger girls come onto the market, she needs notoriety to stay in demand. It's as if she's haunted by the fact that she's sacrificed something she wanted more than she knew for her career. This is what she chose instead, only there wasn't really a choice – but it's all she's got, so she'd better make it work.

Numbed with beer, gin, rum, everything's a blur and her value goes through the roof. As she twirls toward implosion it feels more and more like the final days of Amy Winehouse. But Amy at least had her music to believe in.

✳

And then something turns up to take her mind off the pointlessness.

The Mohocks are a gang of rich, pretty-boy thugs, Bullingdon Club types named after a newly discovered American tribe. Maybe invited by one of her drawling lovers – 'Like to *really* test your mettle, Mrs Salisbury?' – Sally starts to run with the wild boys. There she is, far from her latest bordello in St James's, striding down filthy, lamp-lit streets, the sound of horses' hooves and cursing as the gang hit the criminal rat-runs. Her scented chemise is tucked into men's breeches, muddy riding coat flapping at her ankles, knife in her boot.

One night, two constables catch this bad lad and, rifling his strides for weapons, realise it's a woman. She wriggles away into the dark. Now her fame is stratospheric, though no one really knows if it's her. The only female Mohock is called the "Diablesse". Sally? Who else would do this?

As I can confirm, an unstable background can make staying sane a constant effort. Added to which, the Mohocks can get their hands on drugs. They can pay for hash from the Middle East, ganja from India. Sally's off her head, and about here she comes right off her rocker. Narcotics, lingering syphilis, possibly even lead, the base of her goth-style makeup, which can rot teeth, destroy appetite and methodically send you insane. Maybe the Mohocks like watching her unravel –

she's the only one of them with feelings. 'Dude, look at her. She's hilarious.'

And here's how it ends: at the height of her fame she attacks the one man she cares about, who might genuinely love her in return. Well, obviously. It's just before Christmas, 1722; she's thirty-one. She's going to meet a client and suggests he wait for her at the Three Tuns in Covent Garden's Chandos Place.

The client is a 'noble young person', the Honourable John Finch, son of the Earl of Winchelsea. This is the man she'd told about her love for the fledgling bird, the goldfinch. Though she couldn't say it, maybe she'd been trying to make him see: I love this, your emblem. Jack, I've fallen for you. In her wordy mind the tiny bird might even symbolise the child they could have, a baby finch.

On the night of the disaster, Sally doesn't roll up until after twelve, and goes to join her man, who's in bed in a guest room. He gets up, grabs her, laughing: 'Woah, what day is it? *Finally...*' They sit, talk, flirt. At 2am a boy is called to bring up 'a pint of Frontiniac for Mrs Salisbury', along with a 'French role and a knife'. A pint's not actually a lot for those days, though Sally arrived so late you suspect she was pissed when she got there. I just looked up *frontignac*. A fortified wine like port. As the boy leaves, he hears a row break out.

According to anonymous biography *The Genuine History of Mrs Sarah Pridden and her Gallants*, the next thing is: 'This Virago-lady, finding that the youth whom she most admired had given a piece of paper [an opera ticket], out of his hand, to another of her sex, Her own sister', stabbed him 'with a large keen Scimeter; and then made an attempt upon her fancied rival's arm, covering her with blood but not danger-ously wounding her'.

What? I have to stop for a minute to take this in. Then I hunt dementedly for more detail, and here's what we piece

24

together. Sally's in love, but so wrecked by self-doubt that love can only come with possessiveness. That's number one. Two, her blind sister Jenny, the would-be opera singer, is in the room. If Sally could love anyone truly and lastingly, it seems it was Jen, who we now find has lived with her for years and been protected by her. Turns out Sally felt her sibling might have been vulnerable as a sightless performer, even be debauched by wealthy patrons. The sharper-tongued sister became the breadwinner; knowing she was doing her job for Jenny may have been all that kept her going. On this Christmas night the girls had arrived together at the Three Tuns, Jenny intending, who knows?, to have a drink then retire and leave her sister and her generous friend to it.

But when he gave her a gift, Sally thought Finch fancied Jenny, who was sweeter-natured and not soiled goods. 'You want her, don't you? Is that what you'd like, a blind girl? And *you*, when I pay your keep, and let you trail around after me like a dog...'

They've seen it before, they try to calm her but she's busted. She reaches for the nearest blade and lays into the two people she adores. How could they do this, take away all she has left, make her *hurt* them? She aims with all her strength at Finch's heart. He sinks to the bed with a disbelieving grin. 'Madam, you have wounded me.'

People at the inn that night testify that Sally went instantly from fury to wild remorse – 'Jack, forgive me!' – sobering up in seconds, sending for a surgeon, tearing off strips from her dress to bandage her sister's arm. Asking Finch, a year younger than her, how he is.

'Very bad, and worse than you imagine.' But he kisses her and asks her to be friends with him. Ironically chivalrous: 'I die at pleasure from your hand.' He knows what she's like, maybe understands. And she knows what she's like, and she's sick of it.

Finch eventually recovers and pleads for Sally in court, but it's hopeless. In another life, where she was a well-adjusted middle-class girl, maybe she'd have married him, but Jack would never stay with a woman untamed. Their worlds could only glance off each other, she could only watch him pass. She'd know that.

She's sent to Newgate, famed as a 'hell above ground'. Visitors bring little things to keep her cheerful, but newssheets gleefully report that her health is compromised. She's gaunt. Hair falls out. In May 1723, after a month, she's 'very much indisposed', and by September 'dangerously ill'. Newgate is putrid, and Sally does indeed still have syphilis. On 11 February 1724, she dies. What do the papers say?

> '*Here flat on her Back, but unactive at last*
> *Poor Sally lies under grim Death;*
> *Through the course of her Vices she galloped so fast*
> *No wonder she's now out of breath...*'

Still being fucked then, by Death. Doesn't that make you just want to punch whoever wrote it?

✳

Jesus. This wasn't what I expected. The woman was going to be my hero. I wander outside to our pocket-handkerchief garden. It's wintry and bare but here I am, looking at the sky, not stinking prison walls.

I can't help her now. So is there anything, selfishly, for me in this, which is why I came? Along the lines of: whether you're getting older or are just disheartened, don't want to do what you do anymore or other people don't want you to do it, you have to find a way to live that feels *worthwhile*. Obviously I know this, she must've known it, but knowing it and doing something about it are different. Sally was past thinking how another life might look. What could've helped her? Dunno, rehab? Antidepressants? Seriously. Much as I love her, there must've been an alternative. Why didn't she quit and take Jenny to a cottage in the country? Yeah, right.

And I do love her. Turn back as a chilly breeze slams the door against the wall. Everything that befell her just makes me love her more. She was screwed up but she kept going, even if finally it was in the wrong direction, and she grabbed every heady opportunity – did I mention her stripping off with Viscount Bolingbroke in Greenwich Park, steps from where I am, and running about naked 'in imitation of the deer'?

'Exactly. God's teeth, it's not a sob story, and I'm not here as a lesson. Could you make it quite clear I didn't hate all of it, because you know I didn't.' She regards me. I suppose it's nice to have a bit of balance though? 'Whatever you can make happen, do it.' She nods. 'I'd still say that. Find something or someone that gives you meaning – right now, not what you wanted before – learn about balance from me by all means, but don't sit going over it. Time runs out.'

Yeah. Knowing that and doing it are different. Still, I'm smiling when I close the door. However it ended, that was a ride. And Sally couldn't stick self-pity. If I don't kick myself up the arse, she might reappear to do it for me.

2

As a child, I was radical in my own way. At five I changed the words of 'Baa, Baa, Black Sheep' to 'little girl who lived down the lane'. I got corrected. Well, that boy better be a damned good knitter.

Growing up in the 1960s, there was still an air of the post-war in our house; my mum and dad couldn't get those experiences out of their heads. The little terrace was dark, brown paint on the stairs, cold cramped rooms. Getting hot water was so tricky, a bath was practically the coronation. When I was about six, Mum started helping Dad with his weekly hose-down. His search for building work had reached the point where he was doing patch-up jobs in sewers where rats the size of ponies romped past and, due to this, our awful diet and endless money worries, he was covered in boils that had to be lanced. Bowls full of strips of old sheet covered in blood. And this is hippie London: the dark side.

But I had my own world where I told myself stories, often aloud, and acted them, always the star. In my mind I could look like anything. A wobbling porker, my favourite role was thundering round the playground in Palmers Green being Wonder Woman, whose comic I tore through while guzzling my shepherd's pie. Wonder Woman (Diana Prince, as you'll know from the film) was everything I admired – mind like a scimitar, totally ripped, able to punch out baddies and fly. She was linked for me with Roman huntress-goddess Diana, who was merciless. Only later did I find the DC Thomson cartoon concept really was based on that Roman warrior, mixed with a dash of suffragette Emmeline Pankhurst.

I knew about Roman myth because Mum bought sackfuls of jumble-sale books to keep me and my little sister quiet after we'd finished the available reading matter – mainly the back of Cornflake packets. Astronomy, geography, unspeakable cook-books from the 1950s. Greek and Roman legend. Utterly wild, Diana struck me like a human cannonball. Perhaps that's why Sally Salisbury feels like an alter-ego, reminding me a bit of how I wanted to be. But Wonder Woman was an Amazon princess, Diana was a goddess, even Pankhurst was posh. Sally is my people, a Wonder Woman from a background that made it hard, not easy.

✳

In our house, being untamed was out of the question. Dad was an unreconstructed Victorian who grew up in moody 1930s Holloway, youngest of seven. His puritanical, frankly old-maidish mindset said girls should be subdued, even though his sisters were farting, milk stout-swilling, card-sharping gangsters. Me and my sister, and to some extent Mum, were there to be dominated and refashioned. One of the first things explained to us was that a sense of humour wasn't feminine or attractive, and what we thought was funny wasn't funny anyway, so it was up to Dad to make the jokes. At first I thought these jokes were hilarious. Then I began to realise the people we were laughing at were usually ladies, or people we were saying were stupid who weren't stupid, like everyone French. Mum didn't seem to get the jokes, and a lot of the time she was the butt of them. Her dad, Albert, was French-Canadian, and my mother's maiden name was De la Moule. I can't count the times dad taunted her with the chorus of The Southlanders' terrible song: 'I em a mole and I live in a hooool.' This from a man called Charlie Brown.

When the council demolished our street, Dad decided we'd use the money to start a new life. We moved to a flat above a shop in a Sussex village between Worthing and Brighton. At school, everyone thought my cockney accent was beyond entertaining. I became uncharacteristically quiet.

The shop Dad opened was a failure. In an effort to get away from building he'd come up with a seafront gift emporium selling buckets and spades, seashell ashtrays and little plaster busts of fishermen. Nobody wanted any of it. The frustrated son of a sculptor (an upper-class man who somehow met my widowed nan, loved her, left her with an extra child and danced away), he'd idolised his father on the few occasions he saw him and now began painting seaside scenes on plasterboard. No one wanted those either. More than once ditzy Mum gave someone change for a twenty when they'd given her a ten. The first winter in the shop my bedroom wall, which faced the English Channel, was so wet inside, the horse postcards I'd stuck on it fell off, and Dad found a rat's nest at the bottom of my sister's bed. In February he closed the shop and got his ladders, paintbrushes and spirit level out again, but we were miles behind financially. Mum became a Home Help, then found a job at the bingo hall snack shop until, cash flow destroyed, they let her go.

We moved to a street near the Downs, a bungalow heated by a coal fire and oil stoves you had to drag from room to room, and so basic the taps in the kitchen stuck out of a bare cement wall, but at least it was dry. Mum got another cleaning job, this time at my school. I sometimes saw her arriving just after we'd put our chairs on the desk (so that's why we put our chairs up!) and said our prayers. I wanted to hang around and show her what I'd done, but I was a bit embarrassed, as if she was a VIP. I was impressed to see her talking to the teachers; well, they spoke to her. 'I'm afraid there's paint on the floor again in room 5a, Mrs Brown, and someone was sick in the far corner.'

Meanwhile, I myself was composing. My diaries, a Letts, then a Thirlwell, then a Wombles; stories; essays. In my next to last year of junior school, the QEII was launched. We were taken to the television room to observe the event, then told to write it up. Three reports were best, and mine was second. The joy was eclipsed when the teacher said, 'Are you sure you didn't copy this from Stephen?' Stephen Botterill, looking outraged even though his piece was first, was supposed to be a genius. I didn't even sit near him, so I'd have to have had Wonder Woman's laser vision.

The 60s turned into the 70s. Miss World was a TV regular, women gushing and weeping whether they won or lost. Dad would have the *Sun*'s pull-out chart, and for years, until the horror of it hit me, we'd mark it, every round, evening dress, swimwear – 'Miss Uruguay, look at *that!*' – while Mum sat smoking truculently under the kitchen's striplight. Why did Dad like this stuff, when his morals were so stringent? Because he was a reactionary hypocrite?

Obviously, when I saved enough pocket money for a lipstick, no one could leave the house to go blackberrying until I'd wiped it off. It was like a police state ruled by a bloated despot. But he didn't need to worry. His seaside-postcard tits and bums obsession, the Frankie Howerd 'ooh missus!' when you used a phrase that might possibly be a double entendre – melons, a nice pear, even years later the prospectus for Bristol university – might've made me furious, but I was nearly teenage, his habits were starting to be problematic and my best bet was camouflage. I slopped around in too-big loons and coats that trailed along the floor, gathering mud, dead birds, tin cans. It was better if no one realised I was developing those treacherous female accoutrements. I was dressing like the wife of an Islamic fundamentalist, and I'm almost doing that again now. Though in the interim, of course, I did get over it.

✳

7.38pm.

Steve, weary, lets himself in the door. I've obligingly put broccoli and carrots – about my limit, cooking-wise – on a low heat. He glances up as I trundle down the stairs.

'And how's my little Cabbage Patch doll?'

'With, like, the puffy face and swollen ankles?'

'Did they have those? Well, how's my little Barbie, then?'

'Hm, offensive, because not accurate.' Long legs and nice hair don't stop you being a feminist. Barbie would be early fifties now. She's on HRT, she must be. It's working for *her*. And speaking of age: 'Got a question.'

'Fire away.'

'Would you have sex with a twelve-year-old girl?'

He stops unlacing a boot. 'Are you out of your mind?'

Some men still want it. Look at *Taxi Driver*, Jodie Foster's baby prostitute Iris. 'All right, a thirteen-year-old?'

'Christ's sake.'

Go out to the kitchen and peer into the steamer. 'Why not?'

'Because she would be a child, and I'd prefer a woman. One particular woman, but anyway, a woman. Like any decent man I want adult interaction.' He takes nut cutlets from the freezer. 'Otherwise you might as well shove it in a pig.'

'Like a Tory party scumbag? Well, I hope that's one charming pig.'

'Out of interest...' He gets out the drainer with an air of resignation. 'Are you and me ever having a shag again?'

Right. I wish I could help you, but it's not up to me. So what is it up to? 'Did you know that, apart from the killer whale, humans are the only species where females go through menopause yet remain alive for years and years?'

'Nope. But I've never seen a killer whale as sexy as you.'

Pull up my joggers. Sometimes I wonder if he needs glasses.

✳

I didn't let the Stephen Botterill thing put me off. I wrote stories for my sister, which I read to her, demanding dumbstruck awe. I wrote potential columns for magazines, tearing them to bits in shame – not funny; too long; *madness*. I wrote stories of the sort you might see in Mum's *Woman's Realm*, about painfully vital issues: alcoholic doctors not realising nurses loved them; runaway dogs. There's a lost career there in country music.

In the second year at my comprehensive Boundstone, we had a visit from a careers advisor. I mumbled that I'd like to be a writer.

'I'm sorry, a..?'

'Writer.' Whispered as if by consumptive.

After a moment, while the bulb in the desklamp shone meanly on his nose, he said with compassion, 'Is that realistic? Have you ever written anything?'

I told him I had, and what it most recently was. He smiled over my head at someone. 'I think we'd better forget about that, hm? How about air hostess?' He widened his eyes so I grasped it. 'You'd be flying all over the world.'

I gave it some thought, wondering if my weight might make a plane unstable.

'You need a few O-levels, though.' Taking into account the school I was at, he riffled through a booklet. 'Or – you have nice hair. Hairdresser?'

Perhaps I really was dense because despite this, only months later I got Mum to come with me to the careers evening. There were three boys and one excited chubster with her socks falling down at the stand for the local paper. But though I was first, the bloke from the *Evening Argus* said, 'Sorry, we're not talking to little ladies', and turned to the preening zombie behind me. Mum led me, stunned, away. She hadn't remonstrated. She was proud of my results in English but as a woman who trod a precarious path along the fringes of literacy, it's possible she felt arguing with a journalist put her on shaky ground.

About this time she decided I should get out more. I only had two friends, and I was spending a lot of time in my bedroom, unnaturally reading. I was hardly even watching much telly. Something wasn't right. How could she help me be normal? She started with buying me tights.

These were proper ladies' tights, with a fancy name, Hot Sierra or something, like a Turbo hatchback. Perched on Mum and Dad's bed I looked at myself in the dressing table mirror. Revelation. My legs were nearly attractive. The front door opened. It was two steps from there to where I bounced up and down in an orgy of narcissistic delight.

'Look, Charlie. Her first pair of silk stockings.'

These must be silk! Even if they said *Pretty Polly* and felt quite rough.

Dad stood holding a bucket of brushes in water. 'How much were those?'

I stopped bouncing. Mum said, 'I paid for them, out of my cleaning money.'

'And why does she need them?'

'She's growing up.'

'She's twelve. Don't encourage her to get ideas.' Like growing up? 'We don't want her turning out like your sister.'

I didn't know much about the luscious Joy at that time. So I was listening.

'Oh, not again...'

'That woman's loose.'

I wasn't familiar with the term. She'd been a performer and trapeze artist, allegedly double-jointed; maybe arms falling off? Joy, I later found, recruited by ENSA to entertain the troops, was notorious for having danced on a tabletop in wartime Hong Kong, allegedly without her knickers. Perhaps me prancing in the air rekindled humiliating slurs. Dad's totalitarianism was weighing down on all of us. As I packed away my new tights, I could feel revolt stirring.

3

Here's what I wish had happened next. I'm lying in bed, wondering why I'm a freak living in a freak family, and another whore entirely, Catherine Walters, materialises. Walters had Mum's sunniness and Joy's dangerous chutzpah, and looked like them too, all Dorothy Lamour lips and dusky Liz Taylor curls (yes, but it's true). I wish she'd taken me away, on horseback in the night, galloping as I hung on – or, failing that, had sat on the bed, skirts sighing down around her, and told me it would all work out. I'd have believed her. Living in history's most repressed era, Walters had no interest in being subdued, and none of Sally's unbalanced recklessness.

✳

It's a summer morning in 1858. In the townhouse she owns, 34 Park Street in Mayfair, a gangly nineteen-year-old is pulling on her riding jacket in front of a mirror. The jacket's thin, expensive and tight; she breathes carefully as she buttons the eighteen-inch waist. Bare skin, as many suspect, under the jacket, just a corset to hold her to that absurd hourglass shape. She bundles dark hair into a riding net, fixes a veil over grey eyes and secures a small top hat, compact as Sally Bowles' bowler: her trademark, it's sexy and cabaret. Fifteen minutes later she's in Hyde Park's Rotten Row. Hazy smell of hot grass and dung. She wheels her horse in a circle, attracting narrowed glances from other riders. Catherine doesn't bother about that, needs to make the most of the time; history lesson at eleven, then Latin. Looking forward to it! These are activities she might practise as the daughter of an upper-class household. Then, she wouldn't have paid for them with sex. But she likes sex, will only have it with men she's attracted to. She's more liberated than any girl of her age. It's good to be alive.

There's a lot to like about Catherine, and vast swathes to admire and learn from. As usual, there was luck in there. I'd never say you make your own luck, because too many people work hard and don't get it, but you need to know when to grab something that might turn out to be lucky. What I like most, at least now before I look into her backstory and maybe get my ideals smashed, is her positivity and that measured approach. She made money but on the whole was careful with it; she was stylish in the austere way of, say, Audrey Hepburn, letting her delicacy speak against the stark canvas of a riding suit; she was discreet. She went by an unglamorous nickname, Skittles, which just made her more glamorous, like a beautiful woman shrugging on a man's coat. And not only did she enjoy making love, she was able to love, and not so distractedly that the nature of her job killed her; well, desperate love did happen once but never again. Journalist Henry Labouchere said of her, 'She had the most capacious heart I know, and must be the only whore in history to retain her heart intact.' Finally, her biographer Henry Blyth wrote that she possessed the quality of *being* loved. She was worshipped because she deserved to be. She had the vocabulary of a navvy.

So here we are. Her house, horses, tutor are all paid for by Spencer Compton Cavendish, twenty-five, Marquess of Hartington and the future Duke of Devonshire, who probably met our heroine in Hyde Park. Skittles is an astonishing horsewoman, able to outride most men. One rumour is she'd worked as a circus bareback rider, but most sources say she had a job in a livery stable and was paid to display thoroughbreds on the hunting field. Diplomat Sir Willoughby Maycock wrote that, as a boy, he was trotting home from the hunt with his father at Leicestershire's Stoughton Wood when two riders shot past. One, a female, 'wore a habit that fitted like a glove, and a bit of cherry ribbon round her neck'. As they tore away the girl shouted to her companion, Jem Mason, who fourteen years before had been winner of the 1839 Grand National, that when they got home her arse would be red as the ribbon. The skin-tight gear originated with that job. The stable owner implied to buyers she was naked under the jacket and breeches. She tried it, and liked it.

The education suggests that 'Cav' – bashful, beefily good-looking, being groomed for a political career – is trying to make her wife material. Catherine wolfed down knowledge, and he was impressed with her letters, 'without any mistakes in spelling or grammar. You are getting quite a learned little Skits'.

At this point, she could only be seen in public with him at the hunt. Stories of her daring are legendary – on a bet, she cleared the eighteen-foot water fence at the National Hunt Steeplechase when three other riders had tried and failed. Cav gave her a stable of thoroughbreds, and introduced her to his tailor, Henry Poole & Co, who made her such sleek riding wear people thought she was sewn into it.

The previous year, when she met him, she was already famous as a horsebreaker, usually the term for society girls who rode the fashionable routes like they were vogueing. They drove men mad with lust. Skittles initially kept to quieter paths, putting her animals through their paces, but she was too impressive. Crowds arrived hoping to glimpse her. She gave her name as 'Anonyma', better than Catwoman or Harley Quinn. Jazz virtually played when she appeared.

But the attention begins to drive Cavendish mad. Worse, in 1861, when she's twenty-two, Sir Edwin Landseer delivers his painting The Shrew Tamed, also known as The Pretty Horsebreaker, to the Royal Academy. He uses a model, but the subject is Skittles. A dark-haired girl in a riding habit drowses post-coitally on the hay against the flank of a thoroughbred, which nuzzles her arm. The suggestion: Skittles and her man after sex. The *Athenaeum*'s reviewer misses the point, but still needs sedation: '...the mighty agile sweep of the animal's limbs, his glossy muscle-binding hide; the slender lady reclining fearless among the dreadful feet...' How many feet has this thing got?

Too much for Cavendish's family. By 1862, the cult of Catherine Walters is like a wildfire. Letters in *The Times* bemoan the noisy fans lining Rotten Row trying to see a particular girl ('prettier, better dressed and sitting more gracefully than any of the fine ladies'); the *Telegraph* in a leader thunders that she's a 'worthless and shameful jade', 'selling her miserable body for debauchery'. Cav can't marry her now, and this is explained to him. He's sent to America, writing to her: 'My poor little child... you will see that it must have been done some day...'

She's decimated. Cavendish is putting £500 a year into her bank account, she is suddenly Paris Hilton and there's no need to work, but for her that's not the point. She reneges on her rational spirit and follows him to New York, the only time she'll ever stoop to this. She's trailed like a dog by Aubrey de Vere Beauclerk, later 10th Duke of St Albans, who's left his wife for her, not that she's bothered. She finds Cav and begs, and there's a brief reconciliation. Brief. 'I gave way because I could not bear to see you suffering,' he would write. 'You ask me to come back to you, but you must think darling whether that can ever be possible now...' Ah. He knows she tried to take her mind off things with Beauclerk. He ends it entirely.

In London, she sells everything. *My animals. My home. London. And Cav... that gentle smile.* You remember the good things even about the worst people, and he wasn't that.

Time to go.

And she does, trailing perfume, sadness and resolve behind her. According to diarist Sir William Hardman, once the house is on the market the upper-class women who'd hated and been offended by her, though they'd copied everything she did, 'throng to the deserted halls', pawing what she'd used or touched, 'eager to know how she'd lived and learn the secret of her attractions'. As if.

✳

I once had a black riding jacket, or something like it, that I got from Richmond Oxfam. I even know where it is. Wander to the wardrobe and fish it out. If I've had this for twenty-five years, God knows how old it actually is; the style looks 1940s, the label says, in swooping cursive, John Collier. Nipped waist, no frills.

I like it because it's not looking for a man's attention; it has things to do, achievements to make. Though that's why it gets a certain attention. Take off my holey jumper and slip it on. Amazingly, it's big on me now. Has depression done that, made me thinner? But in the bathroom mirror it's a good look. The dark of it, the shiver and caress of the oyster satin lining, even though that has a rip and I can't sew it together because it's too worn.

Put my hands Bowie-ishly into the narrow slit pockets. I'm pale and my hair, for once washed, is a long pale red thicket.

I could be the ghost of a rider, something that got up and walked away after a fatal accident. But the jacket's still ready. It says, let's go out, let's grab someone's hand and drag them to somewhere or something they don't expect. Let's get on a motorbike or gallop a horse up to Blackheath. Not that I can ride. Strange how something so understated says lust for life. But then like Skits, I've got nothing on underneath. Is it her in my mind, making me think like this? Am I just feeling echoes through the threads of the wilder life I used to have? Or is it echoes of things I still could do?

Take the jacket off, put it on its wooden hanger and close the wardrobe door.

✳

So where did our tough beauty get her drive? Skittles was born in 1839 in Toxteth, near the Liverpool docks. Her dad Edward, an alcoholic who worked at the customs office, would eventually drink himself to death. Her Irish mother Mary Ann Fowler died when Catherine was four, giving birth to her last baby. After a year or two attempting to rear five kids in a very small house, Edward sent Catherine to a remote convent school for the daughters of Catholic paupers. She ran away after a fight with the Mother Superior and got a job back home, setting up skittles in a bowling alley. The pay was low, so she found that additional stables work.

At sixteen, she impressed the honourable George Wentworth-Fitzwilliam while displaying a horse with the Cheshire Hunt. George was thirty-eight, unmarried, and Master of the Fitzwilliam Hounds, which impressed Catherine. Supple as a gymnast, she became his mistress. Easy as that. He brought her to London and set her up in an apartment. The orgasmic ecstasy of comfort, when you'd never had it. Skits was passionate, George may have had a certain talent, and perhaps it was here that she made a crucial discovery; sex was fabulous. The middle- and upper-class lady was expected to be disgusted by it. Catherine, though, was in her element. The affair ended after two years, when a fond Fitzwilliam made her an annual lifetime settlement of £300, with a £2,000 lump sum in the bank. She floated into the arms of Cavendish, and he bought her the Park Street house and all the rest.

And she's leaving it. Adrift without a goal, she heads toward Biarritz. A beautiful boy/man, Wilfrid Scawen Blunt, who looks like Terence Stamp and writes poetry despite his job as a diplomat, is also taking that route, returning from London to his office in Madrid. At Bordeaux, he visits a wayside show entitled 'The Booth of Beauty'. Two unhappy female freaks perform inside; the thing of most beauty, for him, is a girl in the shadowy crowd who clutches his hand when she's unnerved. Outside, he stops to examine a playbill; when he glances up that girl, Catherine, is stepping into the moonlight. She's twenty-four, he's twenty-three – long-haired, unshaven, in bohemian clothes dusty with travel. Seeing himself as a Byronic hero, he feels she's a pagan sprite. That night they walk the streets hand in hand. She talks 'like a running stream', haggles for food in broken French, and in what seems like a fantasy takes him back to where she's staying. She: *'Undid her jacket and anon her dress/With the jet buttons of it one by one/And stood but clothed the more in loveliness... A little goddess from some luminous field.'* Women like this couldn't possibly exist.

When they have sex, his mind is blown. He ends up kneeling, trembling, at her feet.

✳

Biarritz is laid-back, unconventional. They swim, Catherine catches the sun, a working-class thing to do, and parades Blunt openly. Everyone smiles at them. Blunt worships Catherine. He assumes she loves him.

And maybe she does, for a while. She's there by choice, he's not paying her – if anything, she's supporting this dreamy charmer. But Blunt doesn't understand the wild thing he's got. Catherine wants to devour all that the world can offer. In fact, she's decided to carry on working. She's not rich enough to live the way she'd known with Hartington, and she misses it. Plus she enjoys being a courtesan. Spending time with educated, influential men, there's so much to learn.

With Blunt, on the other hand, she's getting bored. One afternoon they're play-fighting over a cushion. Blunt holds onto it a second too long, and sees a flash 'almost of hatred' in her eyes. Over the next days she barely looks at him. Shouldn't he get back to work? Whatever, she's returning to Paris. He pleads for more time, sobbing. Even I want to hit him.

She lets him follow her. Big mistake. Paris isn't Biarritz. Catherine is suited and booted, tousled hair artfully pinned. She begins to establish a circle of cultivated intellectuals and beside them Blunt, in his 'vagabond attire', is tongue-tied and screamingly awkward. She repeats that his job in Madrid is waiting and he buggers off, ashamed.

But it's not over. In August 1864, a year later, he's posted to the embassy in Paris. On his first evening he meets the young daughter of his boss, the ambassador Lord Cowley. Over the following months he gets closer to Lady Feodore Wellesley, so close he's being treated as her fiancé. And then around Christmas a letter arrives. Catherine's been ill, has only just heard he's in Paris. Can he come? He finds his ex-love living in one room, practically broke – still getting the hang of money, she's made a rare misjudgement. She tells Wilfrid the words he longs to hear: she wants to live a beatnik life alone with him, surviving on croissants and coffee. Could he find them a little apartment while she makes a last visit to London?

She leaves him to find them a flat. Days, weeks pass. Then finally here she is, inexplicably back on form, exquisitely dressed and with a lovely apartment on the Champs Elysées.

I need to be based here, she tells a gobsmacked Blunt, but I'll still see lots of you. And on many evenings she comes to his little flat and away they go, arm in arm.

Then one day he blunders into her suite and finds the man who's paying. A letter from her at the time, when she's twenty-seven, is crystal. 'Darling what do you mean by saying I deceived you? I have nothing I want to deceive you in, and if I want to do anything dearest I do it.'

Blunt can't think of a better fantasy than being devoted and destitute with Catherine, but he doesn't come from her background, has no idea what poverty really feels like. He's a trustafarian, born at Petworth House. Would he give that up, flout convention and settle down with a tart? Catherine knows from experience it doesn't always happen; also he's not in line for much, and in the end he marries a wealthy baroness. But it's still now. Days later, he sees her with another young lord, dashes off a histrionic note, and she stops responding.

✳

Do you hate her for messing with Blunt? I can't. When he asks about the money, she's honest, would have told him before if he'd asked. And look at her. Values herself for work she gets a kick out of and a skill she's honed: if you can handle a horse, you can handle a man. Maybe handle life with the same firm touch – race when you can race, pull back if you're going off track. She keeps something inside secure and strong. If she did marry Blunt she could wind up as his property; no independence, stuck in a bridle herself.

What else about her? Probably aware that one day she'd like to retire. Meanwhile travelling, seeing the world. This, remember, is a *working-class whore*. The freedom to manage her life, though so many women at that time don't want freedom. Working on herself to understand things she wasn't taught as a child. And despite a background that might cause emotional issues able to care, and be generous.

43

Could I be like her? Not *be* her, but steal some of that assurance? Was positivity her natural state? Is it anyone's? Some freaks maybe, but... But if you don't have it, and you know that being negative's holding you back and making life rubbish, can you train your mind to be optimistic and keep doing it? Steer it onto a better path? *This* late in the day? Yes, we said we're not giving up. This would be cognitive behaviour therapy, one type I've not had. So instead of trying to work out why you feel scared and gloomy, which makes you think about being scared and gloomy, maybe you picture jumping over the ball of fear like you're clearing a fence. There. Unfortunately, my sense of dread is still in front of me, the size of Beecher's Brook. What if it wasn't a jump but a patch of daisies to canter round; in your head, you paste something lovely where the anxiety was. You could do it on a computer. And so you get that flabby brain – look at it, stuffing Pringles in front of the telly, programming what you feel with the remote – off its bum.

And maybe I really am picking something up by osmosis, because I've felt slightly better since I started writing about Skittles. Slept better. Laughed more. Well, laughing at all at the moment: big thing. But I imagine her laughing, head thrown back, and it's contagious. Occasionally I've even felt a glimmer of assurance about the world. It won't last but it's there, glowing up from the keyboard and into my soul. All from analysing her and thinking about who she was. And this feels like freedom. Is that what positivity is – not chirpiness, but liberation from the shade of depression? Tow that away, you can put anything in its place.

✳

Skittles moves back to London. With cash from that last customer, Kitty or Katie or occasionally Kittsy sets herself up in Chesterfield Street, Mayfair. After a while, she begins writing to Blunt, who with his carved profile and intense gaze had got under her skin. They exchange letters for the next forty years. 'My darling Winny...' 'How are you, old darling?' Resistance is futile.

By her late thirties, Catherine is struggling with lung infections, but still alluring. She begins an affair with Bertie, Prince of Wales, later Edward VII, who she met through Hartington. She grows interested in politics, keeping that mind on its toes. To the point that, when she moves to Mayfair's 15 South Street (there's a blue plaque), she launches Sunday afternoon salons. The Prince turns up, as do Blunt and future Prime Minister William Gladstone, plus a few open-minded female singers and actresses, though no moral woman will go near her.

Her lungs worsen. She returns to the South of France and that's delightful, though 'the sun plays the very deuce with ones eyes and skin... I shall be wrinkled like an old fossel'.

At fifty-eight, she's signing letters Kitty Baillie – not married, just using the name of, impressively, a new lover, Scotsman Alexander Horatio Baillie. He's got no money so it's affection again on her part, and by the time she's sixty-six she's having to ask the now-married Blunt, in an eyelash-batting Felicity Kendal way, for cash. 'I am quite bedridden... As there is no hope of my ever getting better I should so like to see you and say goodbye before I go into a Home.' Stoic in the face of radium treatment for cancer and arthritis, once he gives her money she's back on her feet.

She's amazing, so dynamic that when Baillie tires, or she tires of him, she gets another lover, though this is the last. The honourable Gerald De Saumarez is an artist twenty years younger than her; she met him when he was fifteen and at Eton, and he's waited all this time. With the new pup she's vivacious, purring about her long, thick hair, now white. Picture her risqué cheekiness, the Felicity Kendal thing lingering on. In July 1920, at eighty-one, she told Blunt she and

Gerald were planning to visit Blunt's Sussex home. Instead she had a massive stroke. Her death certificate described her as a 'spinster of no occupation'.

✳

'Can you not just leave things where you drop them?'

I'm racing about bringing in washing when it's raining, halfway through sending out another batch of CVs. I just took the online test to be a postwoman, where you match an address with a postcode. It's timed, it gets faster, and I thought I was doing pretty well – Mrs Tiggywinkle, 5 Death Row, M11. But they turned me down.

I'd planned to apply for shelf-stacking too, but all I can find that I could possibly do is 'general assistant' at a Tesco local in Orpington: 8pm to 8am. I'm finding it hard to camouflage these little bits of bad news with daisies. But I'm trying.

'What?'

'I said, don't leave stuff about! If this wants washing, put it by the sink.'

'I've just got in, give it a rest.'

You probably think I'm appalling. But sometimes I just want to be with these women now. My friends are all at work, and the women are here when I need them. And I almost prefer their company to Steve's. Because with him there's a barrier recently, a corrosive resentment linked to something I haven't told you about.

And yet a grudge is self-defeating, Skittles would be the first to say so. Leap over it if you can, confront it and talk it out. But don't get stuck behind it.

✳

I return to where the jacket is, and look at the clothes at the back of my wardrobe. Some of this is sublime. A shell-pink Rita Hayworth-type blouse with a peplum and mother-of-pearl buttons. An ankle-length chestnut-brown satin skirt with a Victorian feel and emaciated waist that I bought when I

46

smoked and was willowy. I might be able to get that on again now. Why don't I wear it, why have I turned off my glitter? I don't dress like shit all the time, but... most of it. Pull out my underwear bag – not what I currently wear, but the x-rated stuff from years ago. The red and black basques, elbow-length rubber gloves I could probably use when I'm cleaning the cat tray, ripped suspender belts (they've seen action in the trenches) and a mesh body-stocking with what look like carpet burns. Tacky and tasteless, most of it. But not all of it. I can picture Skittles examining this low-cut, apricot balconette bra, which gives you astonishing breasts. She'd love it. That won't fit or look good forever. Run my finger down the soft, suedey slub of the silk and feel some kind of frisson. Ooh. I thought this feeling had gone in me for good. Glance over my shoulder – is it a young Skittles in this room? I can even smell a dark amber perfume. She'd smile, nod, walk over to me, press her chest against my back and hold the bra, or that wine-coloured velvet bustier, up against me; against us both, her body as close to mine as an exoskeleton. And whisper, 'Beautiful. Suits you.'

✻

Skittles never stopped having relationships, though it feels like she was alone in her head even with someone there. Maybe the right man, the one to commit to, never came along, or if he did she refused to see it. So easy to tell yourself the wrong person is right, and the right one's wrong.

Confront the thing. Because allegedly it takes two to tango.

✻

'What you writing?'

Steve, getting a shirt out of the wardrobe at 7.02am as I scribble these pep talks to myself. Eyesight in fact like an eagle's. Wonder whether to save or delete but he's over here in a flash. *'Allegedly it takes two to tango.'*

He steps back, knots his tie. 'That's right. Are you dancin'?'

Well, am I?

47

4

House of love

Is the thing that pays your bills really all you want?
And be strong – but be kind

'He's been talking to me about nihilism. Been reading some very odd books. Wanted to chat about the meaning of life, happiness, the future...' My sister Maggie – waitress, struggling actress and now a theatre outreach worker – texting from her dinky Glasgow housing association flat. My nineteen-year-old nephew, the light of my life, is talking to her about nihilism? Oh no. Could he have inherited that gene from me? At least he's also considering happiness. *'So obviously I mentioned you.'*

Cheers. You told him your big sister's Eeyore.

'Because you're a huge part of my life.'

I'm not actually. It's a long way to Glasgow.

'What part do I play?'

'You're an inspiration. You've always been!'

Sit and stare at this for a moment, then fire off: *'I feel like a failure.'* But I think she's gone to work. The text sits there, looking back at me; my out of shape brain, triumphant again, snorting on its sofa. Then there's a beep. *'A failure?'* Perplexed emoticon. *'How?!'* How long have you got? If I let it, I imagine I'd be surprised my brain, with its greasy fingers, could text so fast.

✳

Failure. Before I became unexpectedly interested in the potentially sexy side of my life, I'd meant to think a bit more about the self-respect those two whores had. Whatever they thought of the morals of their job, they did it conscientiously and were proud of their professionalism. I have just fired off that piece about St Giles. I'll get enough for it to pay for two big shops and six months' flea protection; but that's something.

It *is* something. Because I'm still writing, and earning money from it. People with some sort of judgement publish it.

And everything I did in the past – the hard work, research, resulting broadsheet features – still exists. It hasn't vanished because I don't do it now. Each thing any of us does well is like... a little medal. Just because you're not famous and what you've done hasn't been historically recorded doesn't mean you didn't pull it off. So when I'm walking to Tesco Metro on stinking Trafalgar Road at 7am for Coffee Mate, on my T-shirted chest is pinned my invisible set of awards, stuff I've done that no one can take away – only me, if I undervalue it like I've got into this habit of doing. And while I won't say self-doubt can't be a good motivator – I haven't done enough! Or well enough! – too much fucks up your confidence to do something more, or bigger; or different, which can be bigger than bigger. Maybe it's in league with the working-class in me, saying, that's it for now, love. You've gone as far as you can go.

I am, if only just, doing the job I wanted to do. Dogged, never scared to try again, never chicken... Except sometimes when it all falls into place, and I'm a bit cock-a-hoop. Respect.

✳

Click on Facebook to see if I've missed a private message from an editor asking me to do something, because that does occasionally happen. I used to check it rarely and now I do it all the time just in case, and obviously it's worse than nicotine. At least nicotine helped me concentrate. Find myself distracted even from Facebook trivia – can't hold me – to the ads, crawling up and down the side like Amsterdam call girls, begging me to want them. With my details deep in Facebook's

49

guts, its algorithms are ready to explode with confusion, draping before me stuff about hearing aids and Nick Cave, hot sweats and tattoo parlours, joint pain and hair extensions.

Shaking out today's HRT, wonder if I respect myself for taking these tablets? Well, I had to fight for them, grovelling before a young doctor (Italian, beautiful) who looked at me like I was scrounging for smack. A locum I'd never seen, she considered me as you might a frantic lab rat until I actually did start getting a bit hot. I thought, I'm not going to have this hot flush, not here, not for you. But I did. I talked through it, only once mopping my sweat-soaked lip with my jumper cuff (I didn't have a tissue). She asked if I knew about blood clots and ovarian cancer, and when I said yes and mentioned the depression the menopause definitely wasn't helping, she murmured earnestly, almost hopefully, 'Do you ever think about harming yourself?'

Sigh. I have been over this and over it. I said no because at the moment it pretty much is no. In the past it's sometimes been yes but this is the thing with a locum – you don't want to go through your entire medical history, but as you get older stuff gets more interconnected. Well, I find. So I was sorry to disappoint but, I said, there was no chance of my putting my head in the oven any time soon. Unless I didn't get my HRT or failing that some crack. She slowly shook her head, like I was a very naughty dog, and prescribed anti-depressants.

Would Catherine Walters have taken HRT? Did she even need it? In her sixties, she was crazy in love with someone she'd met when he was a schoolboy. Whereas Steve being ten years younger is actually part of my issue. I used to like it. Toyboy. Only then I started being such a hot mama I was having tropical rainforest flushes, the cries of hoopoes echoing wherever I went.

Hear someone clear their throat, and glimpse a fleeting image of a sultry, grinning face. Skittles? She'd be the first to tell me thinking you're a player is nothing to do with age. Feeling and being considered desirable is about energy, humour, imagination, and the way you see yourself.

✳

What did Skittles have instead of HRT? I start looking up Victorian menopause remedies. Oof. Drinking chloric ether (chloroform, a disinfectant) mixed with distilled water. Opium. Plasters soaked with belladonna, deadly nightshade, held to the pit of the stomach. To what? Numb your worn-out ovaries? Vaginal injections with a solution of lead acetate, which I see has recently been banned in hair dye. If all this didn't help, it was assumed since there was a direct link between the womb and the brain you'd soon be deranged, as if what you'd just been through hadn't done that, so it was off to the asylum.

There's Skittles, leaning against the window frame, arms folded. 'How did I defeat it? Oh, you keep as toned as possible. Exercise. Particularly a certain sort,' she winks, lightly smacks her thigh with a riding crop. 'Posture. Muscles. If you refuse the symptoms of cessation or continue to move your body through them, in time you *will* defeat them.'

Cessation. That was the word, was it: the end? I don't think so.

'That's the spirit. Remember, exercise. Make sure you drink lots of water.'

She probably wouldn't say the last bit, but she's gone. Leaving the perfume I like to imagine, ambery orchid and... what? Hay? Rutting? At my age, Skittles was elastic with vitality.

The menopause is different for everyone, but it might be time to get mine out of its box and chat to it like a nice kitty and even see if it purrs. Because I probably can't be on lovely, potentially lethal Kliofem forever. What's to lose? I can't have less sex drive off HRT than I've got on it.

This is insanity. I was on my knees trying to get this stuff.

51

Well yes, but I've been taking it for ages. In so many things I've never had control, and this is me making a decision. I'll just taper down slowly. And in case my metabolism nosedives, then to my daily bike ride I could add... Running? Hateful, but I'll try. For psychological well-being, smiling instead of scowling (the brain picks up what your face is doing, I read that somewhere) could be therapeutic.

Think I'll stick those things on a Post-It. *Run and smile.* Not together, clearly. I put my pink pill back in its container.

✳

Since I'm taking back control, maybe it's time to look at a few other control freaks, women who grabbed the first female executive position (other than Queen). It's not a nice one, but after the last chapter we can't ignore it. I'm talking about brothel keepers, lady pimps, the women called bawds.

And it's possible from an initial glance that the working-class ones were the nastiest. Nicely brought up Elizabeth Wisebourne, whose stable included Sally Salisbury, didn't seem actively evil. On the other hand I give you steel-hard Liz Needham, picking up girls sleeping rough then charging such huge rent for dresses they had to overwork; Priss Fotheringham, who did *grotesque* things herself as a whore (you think you want to know, but you don't) and presumably expected the same of others; and finally, look out, this chapter's star, Damaris Page.

But you see, I've seen a pamphlet on Page which says her death was followed by 'great lamentation of all the sisterhood'. Unless that's male irony. I saw her listed as an 'unsung East End heroine' in a piece in *The New York Times*, but would they know? There's little evidence for it in their short paragraph. But I've found an etching of someone very like her in Newgate gaol. Standing up in the image is a vision of baby powder-scented loveliness, prison reformer Elizabeth Fry; bit pudgy, actually. Crouching wolf-like at her feet, looking annoyed and exactly like Elphaba, Wicked Witch of the West, is a dark-haired female inmate. Can't be Page, because Fry was around just too late to co-exist with her, but the etching's right here, next to text on Page's life, and because it shows Newgate, her home from home, you just make the link: an impression, showing two of Newgate's finest? Put her name into Google, click on images and you get this one, a welter of bulgy-eyed caricatures – no one knows what she looked like – and a purveyor of 'intimate lingerie'. Some of which is very nice indeed but still, it seems if anyone's going to investigate our grubby friend and find out if she was a bitch or just an early tycoon, it might have to be me. Me and you, thinking about her with what we're trying to make open minds.

Anyone knowing the rumours about our heroine would be speechless at the Pre-Raphaelite sweetheart above, but I found this illustration tagged 'Damaris Page' on a gaming website, filled with mythical and real heroes and villains, and sat staring at it. It isn't her – it's John Roddam Spencer Stanhope's prostitute painting Thoughts of the Past – but it's how the webmistress sees her. Possibly the reason for the hideousness of the original, male-drawn cartoons is that she took control when she'd previously been controlled.

Because Damaris, born in 1620 in London's Stepney, started out as a whore, working the streets as a teenager and picking the surname Page, maybe after her first punter. She was successful, so it's unlikely she wasn't at least slightly attractive. Pretty enough that on 18 April 1653, at thirty-three, she married James Dry at St Mary Magdalen, Bermondsey. If she's married, legally she can't whore, so she stops and looks after Mister Dry. Or so it seems. But just two years later she's in court for bigamy. Someone, maybe James, is claiming she was married fifteen years earlier, at twenty, to William Baker of Stepney. There's no evidence of any wedding to Baker, and Page, admitting the relationship, says the marriage 'wasn't sanctified', and is acquitted. So what's made her accuser trump up this charge?

Maybe it's that she's started working as a madam, getting commissions to fix girls up with tricks – after being a working girl, perhaps she can't stand sitting around begging James for handouts. That's one thing. But at the same time that she's tried for bigamy she's also charged – brace yourself – with killing a girl called Eleanor Pooley, which she did by trying to perform an abortion with a two-pronged fork. I know, believe me, I know. I've no idea if Pooley worked for her or just needed help ending a pregnancy she couldn't afford, but Page does something wrong in the process, and causes an appalling death. Might James have brought both charges? She's convicted of manslaughter and would have been hanged – but she herself is pregnant, and instead goes to Newgate.

If this is James's child, would he want to get rid of her? Or is it someone else's? James is being made to look as though he can't control her, so he reports her: who's in control now?

Conjecture, of course. The baby is stillborn in Newgate, an awful place and not for pregnant women.

Page is thirty-eight when she gets out. She sets up a small-time brothel, renting the property: an entrepreneur position. James dies at some point. Bye, James!

I'd love to say something here about Page's people-handling technique, but all we have is deduction. Many madams, and particularly the one she'll become associated with, Elizabeth Cresswell, have been written about as border-line sadists: academic and author Catharine Arnold calls middle-class Cresswell a 'cruel employer'. Nothing like this was said of Damaris, and there was every opportunity. The abortion won't go away, but who knows the real story of that awful occupational hazard?

1658, 1659... The East End booms. As the city becomes a shipping centre, the docks and wharves along the riverfront at Wapping and Shadwell bulge with dock workers and sailors. Page's gaff is the Three Tuns on Ratcliffe Highway, which runs behind the Wapping wharves and is as much of a stinkhole as it sounds. Damaris runs a tight ship, employing local girls alongside prostitutes who've come in on foreign vessels – Flemish ladies are said to have real expertise. She does well, and ploughs her profits back into a much nicer establishment on Rosemary Lane, near the Tower of London.

Rosemary Lane was derided because it was mainly ruled by women. Not only could females find employment there – running a tavern or whorehouse or working in one – but, because it was a seafaring community where men were often away, they had what historian Margaret Hunt describes as 'an unusual degree of legal and moral authority'. A sailor could give a family member, 'wife', even a landlady a 'power of attorney' to run his affairs in his absence.

East Enders called it having a 'power', and it's partly why so many women got involved in and developed small local businesses like money lending and pawn broking. I got the power? You bet.

But few succeeded like Damaris. Her place on Rosemary Lane catered to naval officers, and she employed classier whores here, possibly including Venetian courtesans, who were too expensive for ordinary seamen and who expected to entertain professionals and aristocrats.

It's a giant leap for Ms Page. It's 1660, Charles II and his big swinging dick are back on the throne, heralding an age of debauchery, and today she saunters down Rosemary Lane as if she scents the boldness to come, pushing through the noisy crowds at the Lane's Rag Fair, where punters can buy second-hand clothes at makeshift stalls. Several shops sell old clothes too – stockings, whalebone corsets – and others sell ships' rigging, brandy, oysters. Reeking of sweet fumes, fish and damp wool, it's a hub of commercial activity.

She smoothes hair off her face, loosens her low-cut chemise and smiles. She'll never be groped again, but she likes to be an ad for what she offers. Her looks haven't gone yet. Ah, sun coming out. Feel that warmth.

✳

'I'm struggling with this latest woman. Still, though I was initially revolted I think I've got a handle on her now where I don't despise her.'

'This is your lady pimp, is it? The seventeenth-century Cynthia Payne?'

We're walking round Sainsbury's, me pushing the trolley. I've got to the vegetarian section. In the adjoining aisles, which we only visit to get liver for the cats, we've passed crowds of people salivating over lumps of naked flesh. I suppose that's what brought the pimps to mind.

'Yuh. I mean, that is what she is so that makes it more presentable, in an unpresentable way. But it's hard. I keep wanting to stop.'

'But she's one of the first female business tycoons? That's impressive.'

'It is. It's just... she's like a one-woman HR department. How do I know she doesn't see women as items on a conveyor belt, the way human resources use people, like one long roll of sausage meat? For HR, humans are like skips or floorspace, a commodity to be rented. That's what she does.'

'One, you're saying this because HR departments repeatedly refuse to authorise your pay on time. And two, who knows when it comes to Damaris Page? You want her not to have been a cow, and maybe she *didn't* treat women badly.' He spins a packet of meat-free chorizo into the trolley.

'But Damaris Page performed an abortion with a fork.'

'Bit louder, I don't think those little kids over there caught the last bit.'

Stare at him. 'You know why that gets to me just now.'

'Yes.' The predictable solid wall comes down. And that's the end of that.

I sigh and say, 'By the way, remember we have to meet Issy Fernandez and her husband for a drink tomorrow.'

'If we must.'

Relax, then grin. 'I thought the Dog & Bone.'

He smiles. 'Nice. Let's see how down with the masses she really is.'

∗

In the car, my mobile rings. My stepmother's name appears, but before I can say anything, her Lancashire voice shouts, 'Who's this? Who's this?' Only six months since she was diagnosed with vascular dementia, and it's getting worse faster than Speedy Gonzales could hijack a cheese factory. Divorcée Deirdre's been married to Dad since the year after my mum died, but she's not actually that much older than me. A shorthand whizz, she was a PA in a local council's finance department on a great *and* regular salary, something new in my family. With costs fronted by his young wife, Dad was finally able to holiday abroad, and they hit everywhere he'd always wanted to go: Egypt, where he was stationed with the RAF, Thailand, Bali, Arizona, New York, Spain; as well as the only place Deirdre wanted to go, Disneyland.

Home or away they hoovered up cakes and pastries, chugging cream doughnuts for breakfast. The most exercise Deirdre took was slouching from the front door to the car, and because she didn't like to walk, Dad sort of stopped doing it too. And this is the result. Deirdre has weathered two heart attacks, has arteries like sewers and now because the blood can't trek through the sludge to her brain, bits of it are dying. Dad's had his own heart problems, culminating in the finale of a triple bypass. When, at fifty, he shacked up with Deirdre, he was able to work a bit less. Once they hung up their P45s, Deirdre accepting early retirement on a sparkling civil service pension, they barely moved (apart from relocating to Devon), and now they can't.

And that's terrible. Speaking about them like this is dreadful. I should care much more, and underneath I must. But my stepmum... can be a tough woman to love, and the northern bluntness sometimes hurts. 'Have you been through your menopause?' she barked at me once, when I was thirty-five and visiting her in hospital during her first heart attack. I shook my head. 'It's awful.' Dad sat fondly holding her hand. 'Everything sags. Your bosoms will be down to your knees. Actually with your boobs, they'll be on the floor.' I handed her the plush giraffe I'd bought her, because she liked that sort of thing. She put it on the bedside cabinet where it sat, staring at me helplessly.

'And don't think you're getting any of my money.' I blinked. 'Whatever we don't use is going to the Lifeboat Association. Isn't it, Charlie?' Dad nodded, smiling. Getting any money from Dad or Deirdre had never occurred to me.

I wonder if having her where Mum used to be is one reason I've drafted in these women, giving me advice. I miss so much, even now, having a mum who wants the best for you, an older woman you can ask for her thoughts. But y'know, I'm an older woman now. So is my sister, and me and Maggie do try to advise each other. These powerful females definitely have guidance for me though, and you can't get much older than someone born four hundred years ago.

Say into the phone, 'Deirdre, it's me...'

'Who?'

✳

The honourable Issy Fernandez is the daughter of a Lib Dem MP. She's got a mockney accent, strongly socialist principles and bought a five-bedroom house in Swiss Cottage for cash at the age of twenty-six. I've worked with her on a few marketing magazines, and she's all right, though we never particularly hit it off. But she's found out I live not far from where she and her new (second) husband now reside, only on the other side of the tracks; she's in leafy Blackheath, we're in concretey East Greenwich. She's Facebooked me repeatedly, inviting us to Sunday lunch. For numerous reasons I don't bother with Sunday lunch, so in the end I told her this, and said I'd be happy to meet for a Sunday afternoon drink. 'Oh, you're the first person to confess they don't adore Sunday lunch,' she replied. 'I so know what you mean. The red wine, the exhaustion of digesting.' Right. It wasn't that, but.

So I mentioned a boozer Steve and I recently discovered. It's dead cheap, full of fabulously eccentric people and their hounds, and filthy.

✳

Bliiiing. A text from my sister. *'Those fuckers at the Office of the Public Guardian have sent all the power of attorney forms back.'* I can tell she's at the end of her tether, and she's good at forms. It's just that the ones we now need for my dad and stepmother are almost incomprehensible. We've tried, and we really thought we'd cracked it. *'I'm going to have to fly down to see Dad and Deirdre again and go through the lot. Then I'll have to post them to you and Steve to countersign. Again. I'm as sick of it as you are. I'm sorry.'*

The very least we can do.

✳

It's blistering on Sunday, gorgeous; an unseasonably warm spring day. Steve and me wander down to the Dog and sit outside, entertained by banter at the next table between a decorator and a bloke with tattoos all over his face ('So I was doin' a bit of pointing the other day...' 'Mate, it's rude to point'). Suddenly a cab appears, and out of it drift Issy and Anton, dressed as if for Ascot. She starts when she sees Boo, the muddy one-eyed bull terrier, under our table – he's not mine, I wish he was – regroups and goes in to get drinks. I accompany her, but she manages to make herself heard over Johnny Kidd and the Pirates ('You don't own me, don't hang around, honey...'). And in the end it's a really nice afternoon until she says, 'So what is wrong with Sunday lunch?'

I look at Steve. Then I tell her my dad, when we were little, had been known to smash a chair if Sunday dinner as we called it wasn't on the table on the dot of 12 midday. He just couldn't help himself. 'I work all week and the least you can do,' he'd roar at mum, 'is make the dinner on time.' Issy pulls down the floaty big brim of her hat. 'I am so dreadfully sorry.' I can see she is, sorry and acutely embarrassed. And so am I, but I can't stop. I tell them about the fights with bread knives between Mum and Dad, late at night, over lack of money; about everyone going on school trips but me. When I glance round, flushed with sun, booze and flamboyant self-pity, I see Steve has his jaw clenched, and I shut up like a vandalised shop.

Issy, breathing deeply, asks what I'm working on now ('Oh, I'm between things'), and moves on to tell us about her new freelance gig. Writing the forms for the Office of the Public Guardian. Steve almost imperceptibly, very slowly, shakes his head at me, but this is something it's all right to talk about! I say we've got a lot of experience of those, and they really need redoing, she can get her teeth right into that.

But as you knew, she's already doing it. The tricky forms are the ones she's produced, though I'm sure they're much better than they used to be. Steve needs another drink immediately, and he goes to get it.

Looking at Anton, who nods and calls for a cab, Issy wonders why we need those forms when Deirdre is only seventy-one, her own mother's age. 'My mother's mind is acute – we're seeing her at the Hampstead Theatre tomorrow. Her body's in pretty good shape, too. Yoga, Pilates, swimming. Interestingly, she eats macrobiotic...'

I think of Deirdre, with her synthetic cream cakes and afternoons spent prostrate in front of *Emmerdale*, or trying to come up with the answers on *Countdown*. Suddenly feel a deep, painful ache of affection for her. Knock back the last of my wine and look round. Issy and Anton have gone.

Wonder if it's okay to cry.

On the way back, lean heavily on Steve's arm. 'So you're going to have a go at me, right?' I want him to. I'm having a go at myself.

'Sometimes you're shameful, but nah mate. You were hilarious. Probably time she heard some of that, being the *Socialist Worker* reader she is. She knows it all goes on, just can't believe someone from your background, and mine, is part of her social circle. Well, was.'

*

We left Damaris with life looking bright. And for a while, it is. By late 1660, she's channelling her profits into property speculation. She builds mansions on Ratcliffe Highway and later in residential areas around the Tower, renting them to high-ranking officials for jaw-dropping sums. She gets to know sea lords and maritime bigwigs who all visit her ladies. And then she makes her mistake, and to please navy bosses agrees to press-gang dock workers.

Which is really stupid. She's already overcharging. Now the working-class men and apprentice boys, amazed she's such a traitor, start pulling her buildings down, alongside other brothels they can't afford.

What come to be known as the Bawdy House Riots kick off on Easter Monday, 23 March 1668. By Wednesday the crowd is up to forty thousand, armed with iron bars, staves, bitterness and frustration. The girls inside these places are supposed to be in Damaris' care. You don't run anything this way.

Eventually it's over. She's been jeered by the mob, been very scared, but she's a determined woman who'll never go down without a fight. She was wrong, and she knows it. She brushes her hair, frowns out of the window, and tries to think.

✳

At fourteen, I'd lost my puppy fat, lost the one friend who could stand my weirdness and was being bullied at school. What did I do? I ran away! Okay, you could say that's chicken, but it took guts, and if it wasn't an inspired solution it was the only one I had.

So that's me, there, on the verge of a nervous breakdown, climbing out my bedroom window one winter morning then lumbering off to the rec, where I sat anxiously on the swings, then went home. After Mum and Dad had been to see the headmaster I got referred to a Child Guidance group, where a load of other kids who didn't fit in painted, drew, sat humming in a corner, told stories about how easy it was to walk straight in front of a car, or listened to assorted 45s on an old record player, and where we were supervised by two trippy freaks who seemed a lot less sane than us. I was ashamed when the secure van came to pick me up every other day, diving off the seat in case anyone from school saw me but, despite it all, eventually I didn't mind going. There was no more O-level pressure; all we had was our remedial work, we might as well have been crafting raffia baskets. It let your brain slowly put itself back together. They kept us in a big (if locked) room in Worthing and I was free to write efforts at features in my collection of notebooks. Until the woman, Veronica, came across them. 'Cute, she's been writing stories. Listen to this one, folks...' I asked for my book back. 'Ooh, full of secrets?' At that moment, I knew I was ready to leave.

I hadn't been totally uneducated during this year. To give Dad credit, he'd found time amid a job involving ten-hour shifts of manual labour to work out lessons for me. I also started going to the village's tiny library to read *Spare Rib*, but its humourlessness made being a woman seem harder work than crushing rocks. If only I'd heard of *Ms* magazine and its kick-ass editor, ex-Bunnygirl Gloria Steinem. There's a true Wonder Woman – in fact Wonder Woman was on the first cover, because Steinem also grew up revering her.

But I had a Wonder Woman of my own: Mum. She hid her magical forces in a shapeless mock-sheepskin jacket and wellingtons, but it was she who told me, one afternoon when I got back from Child Guidance, that she'd found me a place on a typing course. The youngest there, I got taken under everyone's wing. From backgrounds as bad as mine, the girls had bitten nails, hoop earrings, push-up bras, and treated me like a mascot.

Dad was over the moon. I was training for a job, and soon I'd be bringing in money. He and Mum relaxed a bit. One warm spring evening he brought home a brick of Wall's vanilla. Their treat was a slice of ice cream in a glass, filled up with cream soda. Dad was a bit of a singer, any old thing. Now, as Mum sipped her mush, he charmed her with a Fats Waller gem. I don't even think he'd had a drink. 'Oh I'm the sheek of Arr-abee, your love belongs to me/At night, when you're *asleeeep*, into your tent I'll creep (you lovely thing!).' Mum glanced at him – she was still, in her forties, so pretty, black hair and blue eyes like Snow White. Well, I'll always think that.

'The stars that shine above, will light our way to love...' Dramatic wink. 'You'll rule this land with me, baybeh, the sheik of Araby.' He took her hand, she resisted then put down her glass and they danced over the lino as my sister giggled and I rolled my eyes. Dad had issues. Still, this was nice.

I practised my typing on Dad's black Remington, huge as a church organ and when you pushed down a key, your finger felt like it was never coming back. I developed muscles from carrying that thing to the kitchen table. I got faster and faster.

✳

Here's what Damaris comes up with. She goes to see that piece of work Liz Cresswell who, nicely brought up, doesn't feel the same pain as Damaris at having overcharged the workers. For her, the next step is just about profile.

They sit down and write *The Poor Whores' Petition*. Addressed to Lady Barbara Castlemaine, King Charles's lover and mega-shopaholic, it demands this sponger help out her 'sisters' and give anyone who needs it the cash to rebuild their brothel. It addresses Barbara as the queen of tarts ('the most splendid Lady of Pleasure'), and signs off with the details she might need, saying this comes from the 'undone company of poore distressed whores, bawds, pimps... Signed by us, Madam Cresswell and Damaris Page, in the behalf of our sisters and fellow sufferers (in this day of our calamity) in Dog and Bitch Yard, Lukenor's Lane, Saffron Hill, Chiswell Street, Rosemary Lane, Ratcliffe Highway...'

At the end, in case she thinks the mob respects her, they promise, 'Should your Eminency but once fall into these

Rough hands, you may expect no more Favour than they have shewn unto us poor Inferiour Whores.' Because you're just like us, only we're the *people's* whores. And if Damaris hadn't been, for a tiny blip, she is now.

Everyone hears about the letter and loves it, and Page is seen as decent after all. Close shave. But the whole steep learning curve changed her.

Years later, Daniel Defoe based his novel about the prostitute Moll Flanders, many think, on Damaris. It's not the story of a monster, but of a desperate, basically decent woman who resorts to sex, stealing and cheating to make her life work out because there aren't many other choices. In one of the movie versions of *Moll Flanders*, she's played by a red-haired Kim Novak.

✳

I wangled myself a kind of breakthrough, too; only I couldn't use it. I'd had a response to a letter and column I'd sent to *Look Now* magazine, where my idol was writer Jill Eckersley. The editor, Richard Barber, wanted to meet me. So me and Mum negotiated our way to London, to Newman Street off Oxford Street, where I was shown around the magazine, met Jill Eckersley (Jesus) and had a chat to Richard. Who offered me a job as a sub-editor – I was nowhere near good enough to sit at home and write columns. What Richard didn't know was that I was fifteen, below school-leaving age. Plus, Mum had got me on this typing course; I had to finish it, I didn't have a single qualification. 'Up to you,' he smiled. 'Keep in touch.' Well, more opportunities would come. They must.

So I got my RSA typewriting Stages I and II. I got a receptionist job in a tiling company (the secretary in accounts: 'Take that tea back and make it again, you know that's not how I like it. Has she made yours right, Joan?'), and then one at the HQ of a domestic appliances firm. Taking my weekly rent, Dad had no idea that, when he thought I was revving up my typing speeds, I was still sending off columns. Which all came back, but whatever.

✳

'You took a job in a tiling firm when you could've been working as a journalist off Oxford Street?' Damaris is by my desk, the receipts drawer open, casting a jaundiced eye over last year's accounts. 'How many of us have to tell you, don't sit *gazing* at opportunities. Even now, you don't see them for what they are. Up to you to find the prince hidden in the beast of, say, your Bawdy House Riots or your "we're letting all freelancers go" email. Then sink your teeth in.'

Sink my teeth into the prince?

'Princes don't come along often.'

You're telling me.

'God knows how long you're going to wait. Unless you're scared to try doing what you actually want in case you're crap and balls it up.'

'Er, yeah.' I can't risk it, not again.

'Though it's unlikely to work out first time. Or second.'

'You don't say.'

She focuses on me. She's shaved her eyebrows and drawn in skinny arches like a Biba model. 'Watch your tone. You think I'm reprehensible, don't you? Even you. Like I care, don't you think I'm used to it? But I have a string of properties. What do you have? I have men – oh, you thought because of my work I can't feel love or enjoy it? But I do. What do you have?'

Cheeky. Blow my nose, run through Facebook for a minute and she's gone.

✳

The riots took their toll though. Page's health went downhill. At forty-nine she was put away in the horrorshow of the Marshalsea prison, on what's now Borough High Street, where the jailors were fond of thumbscrews. She became ill and on

66

9 October, only eighteen months after the Riots, she died, leaving her fortune to her sister Margaret. She'd worked too hard running a business to have a family, if she even wanted one.

✳

Why did I waste my life at that tiling company? And I've stuck it out in worse places. It's so handy to do a rubbish job if it buys you space to get your side hustle off the ground, but so easy to get stuck there. Years can go by, and one day you might want them back.

✳

'What've you done today?'

'Damn all, apart from a bit of thinking.'

'Good. You needed a rest.'

'Is that a joke? I'm barely working, I feel terrible.'

He rakes back hair, looking at his phone. 'Oh, you always feel terrible. You're a better Catholic than I ever was. By the way, I'm out tomorrow night.'

'Again?'

But he's disappeared to the bathroom.

5

Don't act like you care

Invent yourself – the possibility's always there

The doctor this morning is new, as usual. Chinese and soignée. She's lovely. She listens to the story of my assorted issues, which again I take from the top, finishing with my need to visit the bathroom, just to see how it's doing, all night long. 'I think we need some bloods,' she says. 'In fact, a full blood count wouldn't go amiss. But my first inclination is you give up the HRT. You've been cutting back. Take your last one tomorrow, then stop. Can you do that?'

While I'm wondering she says, 'And when I see you next, perhaps make a double appointment and I'll examine you internally. It *might* be something like vaginal atrophy.'

Bug-eyed, head back out to unlock the bike.

Vaginal atrophy. Great name for a band.

✱

At seventeen I knew – as I fielded calls about Hotpoint dishwashers and booked in the number of Miele fridges at each shop – that I could do a bit more than this. As my mind exploded with the Keats, Shelley and Kurt Vonnegut I found in thrift shops, I realised I was ready to do those O-levels. Mum found a Further Education college in Chichester and I got in just as term was starting.

Off my head with happiness, I soaked up knowledge, scribbling at my converted dressing table. Dad found it inexplicable. He told mum to drag me away from my books so I could 'stop being stuck-up and watch telly like a normal person'. To avoid confrontation I did it, sitting in my chair in the front room but with my back to the TV, fingers in my ears, still reading. My most delirious point was one of the moments the electricity ran out, this time during *Starsky & Hutch*, because it was hard to ignore a show that good and I'd been very tempted to watch. To the slow 'wuurrrr' of an engine dying, the lights went off, the kettle stopped boiling, the screen went blank, and I grinned in the shadows as Dad cursed and scuffled around trying to find a ten-pence piece for the meter. Hah, he didn't have one! He'd have to go to the shop, buy some Rizlas and ask for change. Unless he sent me or Magz, but we could take ages, and he was missing smirking at Huggy Bear, who might be black but was bloody funny. In the dark, I tested myself on Macbeth speeches.

✳

And then, in an English class, where every week a few people were asked to read the next scene, I got nominated for Lady Macbeth. I wasn't our family's actress, that of course turned out to be my Bonnie Langford-style sister. I stared at my shaking hands, but I did it. And because I'd studied so hard; because I'd fallen in love with Shakespeare as he paced my tiny bedroom, feverishly explaining his works to me; and because I'd just written a controversial essay asserting that Lady Macbeth, distraught but resigned, had to do almost everything for her inept husband so that he got what he wanted, I poured my heart into it, reading from my desk, while Chris something, laconic and handsome on the other side of the room, read Macbeth. As I whispered and growled out the words, I heard something respond in his voice.

When we finished there was a horrified hush, then a clamour. 'Lady Macbeth is not like that!' I sat silent, wondering if madness was something we shared, and what Lady Macbeth's Christian name was.

'How d'ya know?' Our tutor Martha, a glorious, laid-back hippy, was grinning. She applauded in my direction, and Chris – he met my gaze with his own, and instead of our usual mateyness it was full of... other things entirely. This was what words could do, if you believed in their strength. This was what your mind could do. Not ready for Chris – he was twenty-eight! – I carried on being a friendly dork, and the frisson dissolved. But now I knew I had another sort of strength. Not the kind my background said women needed, about looking after a family, but maybe intelligence, which it explicitly said we shouldn't have, if we wanted to be wanted. And it worked with a kind of man I hadn't really believed existed. Happiness was to do with thinking, and in my own odd way.

As I walked out of that room, I understood a couple more things. First, that you could reinterpret the world, like you could with a play; there were a million readings, and it was up to you to choose yours. That's what everyone did – though sometimes they chose a version (or had one forced on them) and stuck with it even if it made them miserable. And second, in a similar way and by acting, you might be able to choose who you wanted to be. If you didn't like who you were, you could invent a new part. You just had to make everyone believe it. Once you believed it yourself, you were done.

Lady Macbeth, of course, would originally have had to be played by a boy, square chin, big hands. Actresses were only,

70

finally, allowed on the stage in Charles II's time. At first their reputation was questionable; women prepared to display themselves like this *must* be immoral. Since no female of distinction would tread the boards, however highbrow the production, it was left to the scum to grab their chance, to get up there and educate and express themselves and sometimes, to their astonishment, soar. If they were useless they were sacked, so they had to work to understand their role, and play it with emotion and conviction. These women were bright and, because of a tweak of fate, they got a chance to show it.

Eleanor Gwyn is born on 2 February, 1650; ten years later Charles, twenty years older than her, is restored to the throne.

The timing is perfect in terms of their relationship; probably the only perfect thing Nell's mother ever did. When I was growing up, Gwyn was a kind of joke, your fruity, booby orange-seller; but people know about her because she was Charles's most magnetic mistress, her personality making her as memorable as him. She got the part of the mistress by being a knockout onstage – according to historian Elizabeth Howe, 'the most famous Restoration actress, possessed of an extraordinary comic talent'. Because of her terrible background, she was also one of the few mistresses Charles couldn't create duchess of anything.

Like Skittles, gutter rat Nell was insufferably buoyant. That can't be because she was insensitive, a thick-skinned woman couldn't pull off such drop-dead phrasing. Reborn now, it's possible she'd be Gemma Arterton, who in 2016 brought Nell to fizzy, feminist life in Jessica Swale's West End play, and who was born in Gravesend to a cleaner and a welder.

Nell's start was somewhat tougher than Arterton's. Several places she might have been born include cramped Pipe Well Lane in Hereford, now Gwynne Street; and Coal Yard Alley, a Covent Garden slum. Her dad, possibly a soldier broken by the civil war, became a brewer and wound up in debtor's prison, but he was long gone by the time Nell was two or three.

'Yes, gone, not missed, what else? Come on, darlin', ain't got all day.'

All *right*. Nell already, here in my head? So Nelly and big sister *Rose*, who later marries a highwayman ('slow down!') grow up with Old Ma Gwyn, also known as Helena, an obese, brandy-swigging drunk eventually found dead in a pond, but who before that runs a brothel. The girls, both handsome (Nell was slight, boyish, face like a young Mick Jagger) were probably child prostitutes. Because Nell never seems beaten down, it's possible the brothel was a riotous but not vicious place and the girls thought they were being 'looked after' by these tawdry uncles. When they aren't working here, Rose and Nell sell herrings, oysters, turnips and cinders. Cinders? 'Collected from gas works, sold door to door, keeps a fire going. This isn't the best bit.' I think some of it is.

In 1662, when Nell is almost thirteen, she finds a man who wants her on a more exclusive basis, probably because she's cute as a button. Robert Duncan, an officer in the guards, sets her up in rooms above a pub in Maypole Alley, between Drury Lane and the Strand, the location presumably because he's interested in managing a theatre being built nearby.

And so it begins. During the previous decade of Puritan rule, 'frivolous' pastimes like going to the theatre were banned. Corrective early acts passed by Charles include the licensing of two performing companies and that shocking legalisation of acting for women. In 1663 the King's Company, led by Charles's friend Thomas Killigrew, open at Killigrew's playhouse in Drury Lane, now named the Theatre Royal. Duncan can't talk about anything else. Nelly lies on her side, cheek on her fist, and listens. 'I'd like to see it, Mister Duncan. Is there any little job I could do there?'

Nelly and Rose are quickly recruited as half-dressed 'orange girls', selling small, sweet 'china' oranges – yes, imported from

China – at sixpence each. Standing in the wings Nell watches the actors, distracted by the make-up, banter and thrill, by the dash and articulacy of the men and the fact that they treat women like her, the few who act there, almost as equals, even seem to like the novelty of a woman playing a woman.

'Oi, Nelly! Oranges to sell!'

But I could do what they're doing. Familiar story.

Out in the audience, sigh, vending, she gawps at London society; this is the 'King's playhouse', and Charles is here a lot. She's in the same room as the king. There he is! Don't stare. She stares.

So here is Nell: showing off her pocket Venus legs in a skirt hitched on one side up into her belt, hair falling over her face as she hands you an orange. But what makes you stop talking or if you're in the pit, throwing food, and look at her is her wit and strong, clear voice. Killigrew would have to be blind not to notice. 'Who is she? They actually are eating out of her hand.' Within a year, she's recruited into his group of actresses. She'd been showing off to get his attention but now she's in over her head. She can't read or write, is handed a script and stares at the marks on the pages. 'Let's hear you, Eleanor.' 'Yes. Just let me look at it privately for a minute...'

But Killigrew is not surprised and, seeing potential, puts her in his acting school, where she's taught by Charles Hart, one of the finest performers of the day. She's fourteen, Hart is thirty-nine, and soon he's her lover. He reads her the lines, again and again, long after the rest have left, as they pace the stage in the candlelight. 'And then what? Eleanor, what is your line?'

She makes her debut in 1665, at fifteen, in John Dryden's heroic drama *The Indian Emperor*, playing Cydaria, daughter of Montezuma. Big mistake. Pepys sees her in the same role two years later, and she hasn't improved. 'Saw the Indian

Emperour, where I find Nell come again, which I am glad of; but was most infinitely displeased with her being put to act the Emperour's daughter; which is a great and serious part, which she do most basely.'

She knew it. Nell is a funny girl, a mimic with a gift for repartee, not a tragedienne. Luckily, the racy, brand-new style that is Restoration comedy is perfect for her, and in it, in the interim, she becomes a star. Two months after that first desperate performance she appears opposite Hart in *All's Mistaken or The Mad Couple*, 'mad' used in the sense of wacky, really. They play sparring lovers, along the lines of Beatrice and Benedick in *Much Ado About Nothing* or, much later, Elyot and Sybil in Noel Coward's *Private Lives* – even maybe screwball comedy *His Girl Friday*'s wildly droll journalist Hildy Johnson, my all-time heroine, with Walter Burns. Total triumph. Nell can deliver deft, withering asides to the audience, she can outwit and belittle her posturing man and have onlookers helpless. She must've almost cried with relief. I *can* do it. *This* is what I'm good at!

Everyone can see it. She's given the risqué, fashionable pro-logues and epilogues of plays to deliver, and brings the house down. Crowds come for her alone, and Dryden begins to write characters with Nell in mind. One of these, in March 1667 when she's seventeen, is sexy, irreverent Florimel in *Secret Love or The Maiden Queen*; a breeches part where Nell's character impersonates a boy and wears tight-fitting trousers. It drives the audience out of their minds. Pepys sees the play at least three times; obviously, just to make sure he under-stands it.

And the more he sees her, the more worked up he gets. That October he's at the theatre to meet his mistress Mary Knipp, horse-dealer's wife and actress. 'She took us up into the tireing-rooms and to the women's shift, where Nell was dressing herself and was all unready, and is very pretty, prettier than I thought... But lord, to see how they were both painted would make a man mad; and what base company of men comes among them, and how lewdly they talk!' Nell is bantering with hip young lords, who lounge in chairs, fixated by this clever, preoccupied ('Stay or go, I've work to do'), half-naked girl. She runs through her part, rouges her cleavage, in a moment will control an audience. Pepys's wife must've wanted to punch her.

But Nell is soon lifted to another level entirely. She'd begun to socialise with the upper class during a short affair with Lord Buckhurst, described as 'cultured, satirical, dissolute and charming', so probably she learned even speedier verbal jousting. When she's eighteen, a young aristocrat takes her to the theatre in Lincoln's Inn Fields. By now she's famous. Her date's got cash, so she's in a box. Who is in the adjoining box? The king and his brother. It's like finding you're sitting next to Prince William, before he was married, out on the lash with Harry. It's a bit like – really – a Restoration version of *Love, Actually.* She turns, blinks, looks away. Gazing as if rapt at the stage, she lets the shoulder of her gown fall lower. Moistens her lips when she knows Charles is watching her, which he spends most of the evening doing. And when he's definitely looking, she looks at him, for some time. Quite understandably, when the lights go up, the king and his brother James invite Nell and her friend to supper.

'And naturally they had no money. I had to pay. I told Charles this was the poorest company I ever had been in.'

It was April 1668. By summer, the Gwyn/Charles affair is well known, though like all his flings, is expected to be short. She carries on performing, drawing massive crowds. Playwrights vie to write for her, and she learns her lines and plays the parts commandingly as her expressiveness grows. But the more the king wants her by his side, the less time there is for career.

Charles has a harem of mistresses, but few can match Nell. The favourite, Barbara Palmer, Lady Castlemaine, is not just manipulative but 'enormously vicious' and wilting with age. Soon there would be delicate, grasping, humourless Louise de Kérouaille, a noblewoman from Versailles Nell nicknames 'Squintabella', or 'Weeping Willow' for her fits of woe, caricaturing her French accent so the court struggles not to guffaw. The only other mistress with talent is actress Moll Davis, who's worked hard to be taken seriously in tragic roles. But Davis has lost her heart to Lord Rochester (played with unnerving degeneracy by Johnny Depp in *The Libertine*), who bet his friends he could make her an actress, coached her, got her pregnant, then dropped her. Of course she's good at tragedy.

Nell is given rooms at court. At twenty, she has a baby, Charles, and the following year retires from the stage. Her role with the king is as challenging, and full-time, making up her own lines. Though some of this is starting to be who she is; having bent her mind to demanding roles she's altering, appreciating finer nuances, her speech more eloquent.

Uncategorisable, now you can't class her at all. She keeps the king's interest, the only woman who does. And not only is she clever enough not to bore a clever man, she loves him. Again, probably the only woman who does.

Finally, though she dresses exquisitely, gets a townhouse in Pall Mall and the lovely Burford House in Windsor, she hasn't asked for these. Having lost her second son when he was ten, what she does want is something for Charles junior, and is delighted when he's made Earl of Burford.

Charles II dies in 1695, and his famous last words are about Nell, that she should be looked after ('Don't let Nelly starve'). She remains faithful, taking no other lover, sadly telling a would-be suitor that she'd never 'lay a dog where the deer had laid'. (When Charles was still alive, she'd slapped the Duke of Buckingham for trying to kiss her.) She dies less than two years later, at thirty-seven, of a series of strokes probably due to long-term syphilis.

'He was worth every second. At the start, obviously, living at court meant performing, but the behaviour became habit. I wanted it to work, and I'm good. Acting's what you should do. Act as if you take things lightly. Act like life's a laugh, because most of the time it is.'

For you maybe, silk dresses and houses in Pall Mall. My life's not a laugh, some of it's been a joke.

'Victim mentality, I thought you were working on that.'

It's impressive how each of these women is trying, in her own way, to sort me out. Like I can't accept I could do it for myself. The affirmation Post-Its all over the walls! Though of course life changes, and what got you through one part doesn't necessarily work for the next. One Post-It fell on my head at the desk yesterday. 'We are what we repeatedly do.' I stuck it back with Blu-Tac. Eleanor picks an Easy Peeler satsuma from the bowl, attacks it with bony fingers. 'This comes off nice, like a loosened corset.' Chomps a segment. 'Ooh! No pips.'

Mine would have pips. 'Because you want it to!'

She wipes her fingers on a teacloth. 'You think being one of twenty mistresses was funny? Having a boy die at ten?' I forgot. 'But as you know, because you've got the books to tell you, you can be cheerful every day, or miserable. At least you've got days. By the time I was your age, I was dead.'

So that's really it? Each morning, the option to be gloomy and preoccupied, or happy and hopeful? So you pick happy, or act like you are, which sounds even more exhausting because it's a lie.

'Jesus Christ. Yes, pretending is tiring at the start. But you could wait forever if you want to go Method, which is the equivalent of analysis. And did analysis work for you? Forget motivation. Act the part til it's second nature.'

If you knew how much I want to do that. Turn off the computer and drag out my horrible running shoes. Seems dark. Is it going to rain? Not on my fucking parade.

'For once! That's the idea.'

✳

Thud thud thud in the rain. I'm really making an effort to shift the depression, to be positive as Skittles and now Nell, but it's been like pushing away a boulder.

Well, let's try again. *Act happy.* If you like these characters, copy them. Hear a squelching sound and see, beside me, Nell Gwyn, running in wet velvet shoes, pushing Charlie jnr – sorry, the Earl of Burford – in a stroller. Let out a guffaw. I am mental. My brain is amazing, think what it could do if wired right. The kid's delighted, bashing the plastic rainguard with small red fists. 'This is a lark, innit? Hard work with the skirt soaked. See how desperate for help you must be?' I slow down, panting, to a walk, and so does she. Look at the gurgling boy. 'No, you don't have one of these. You'll have to come to terms with that. And you don't have the other thing, a book.' How does she know?

'But look what you do have.' She gestures back in the direction of our terrace. 'A bit of independence, the place you live. And you didn't earn it on your back.' In a touch of pathetic fallacy, the sun edges past a cloud to shine down roughly where our tiny house is. She bends to examine her shoe. 'It's your life.' And this time, she really is gone.

✳

After surprising O level results, a lecturer asked what I planned for A levels. When Dad got wind of the fact that I wanted to spend another year dossing, he kicked a chair right across the kitchen, then sat on it miserably. 'I can't afford this. Look how much she's cost me already in food, gas, electric.'

God knows how Mum convinced him, but she did. I ripped through the nine-month A-level course, obsessed now

78

with *Othello* and having to be dragged from my room for Sunday dinner when I was halfway through the library's 33rpm version of the Paul Schofield production. *Cold, cold, my girl...* 'Would you know how to cook this dinner your mother's made? Wouldn't that be a bit more useful?' That year I won a little silver cup for my student magazine poems, but you can't make a nice roast dinner out of one of those.

The final straw came when, as we neared exam time, a tutor asked why I was the only one not applying to university. Mr Phillips, the English teacher, explained what I might get out of it ('I think you could teach at an American college...'). It sounded phenomenal, compared to the tiling factory.

I left Mum to broach it with Dad. At least if I got into somewhere, I wouldn't be living at home so I wouldn't be costing him money. This was the era of student grants; Mr Phillips made it clear I could probably get one. When I gave him the figure my father supplied to me, under duress, as his annual earnings, Phillips laughed aloud. 'He's made this up. No one earns this little.' So Dad was lying? Or Phillips was sheltered. Or both.

✳

The weather's turning. Springtime is coming. Steve is getting up earlier, fucking about in front of the mirror with aftershave and now moisturiser, then he's gone, sometimes before I've come to wave. At night, he gets in late. I text him a few times as darkness falls. 'Anything I can cut up for you?' Like our life together? Or have I already done that?

✳

When I got my A-level results, Mr Phillips zoomed me through clearing in a desperate bid to get me into the place he'd gone. He'd done something else very kind, actually, inviting me one Sunday to the home he and his wife shared near Fareham. I arrived for what they called lunch and found a ferociously intelligent thirtysomething couple in a book-lined

79

Georgian terrace. Lunch was not easy. I sat paralysed, staring at the rows of spoons and forks either side of my plate, until Mr Phillips said, 'Start from the outside and work in.' Now I think, did they really live like this, the two of them? Or – God – was it to teach me basics I might need later? Once that was over, he took me to his office and talked me through the books he was giving me: the *Oresteia* by Aeschylus, *The Iliad*, Plato's *Symposium*. I doubted I was up to it, but as I began the *Oresteia* on the train, my heart pounded to the rhythm of the lines.

Clearing. Jaw rigid, hands wet on the wheel, Dad drove me and Mum to Bristol for my interview. I walked down echoing halls in the Wills Memorial Building, financed by cigars, sat and talked about TS Eliot in a dark room, and the two pleasant lecturers asked me, since there wasn't time to sort out a grant, what I proposed to do for money. As I tried to come up with an answer, the button I'd been twisting on my Etam jacket fell off. They said they'd offer me a place if cash wasn't a problem; I should reapply next year. When I emerged, Dad exploded. 'You've dragged us two hundred miles for *nothing?*' He ranted all the way down the M4, until we had to stop at the Leigh Delamere services for Mum to throw up with her usual migraine. What we thought was a migraine.

I got two offers for the following September, at Exeter and Reading. Mum came with me to every interview. Returning along a corridor after spouting some rubbish, I saw her waiting at the end, still where she'd been two hours earlier, sitting on an uncomfortable chair holding her carrier bag and trying to seem inconspicuous. No one had even offered her a cup of tea. She was wearing her wellingtons. Perhaps they thought she was the cleaner? Of course, she'd brought a flask of milky coffee and some home-made rolls filled with cheese and Marmite, untouched until we got on the train where, chomping, I giddily recounted every detail of what had been said.

Tougher than she looked, wreathed in smiles, she was my determined guardian angel.

I went for Exeter, and it worked out great because I'd have time to save up in my gap year. I accepted a job as team leader at Cresco, which sold paper towels ('Just try to turn this down,' said the guy who interviewed me. 'Fantastic salary and all the paper towels you can carry.' He shrugged. 'Take some for your family even.') In the nick of time I found something better, in Hove, and started work the next week as a trainee building society manager.

6

On the bike, pass something in misty, ghostly grey, crumpled on the pavement. A kitten-soft scoopneck jumper from the Marks & Spencer Autograph collection. And it's cashmere. Stuff it surreptitiously in my bag. At home, wash it in Lux Flakes, marvelling at its downiness. When it's dry, fold it away. Treat it like a pedigree, peeking in to stroke it. And at the weekend, put it on with my black leggings and a vest top, then hitch my hair into a loose bun. Walk downstairs. Steve, reading on the sofa, looks up and whistles. 'Woah. Is this a ballerina in the house?' I don't normally get this. He stands up and hugs me. 'What's the grey thing made of?'

'Cashmere. Found it.' Mumble, 'Someone must be looking for it.'

'Found it where?'

'Hyde Vale.'

One of the most expensive streets in Greenwich.

He shrugs. 'Well, put it back if you like, but if they live around there, this is probably one of a wardrobe full.'

It is. I bet it is. So shamefully I don't return it to where it was, but spend the day in it, caressed by it and feeling... very different. Feeling like a woman – a ballerina, probably French or Spanish – who wears a loose cashmere sloppy joe after her day at the barre. Even in Costa I feel sophisticated. Even in the pub. These days, I could never buy something like this new. If I ever could.

Less than a week later, again heading up Hyde Vale, notice a skip. I mean, they're throwing this stuff away. As I pass, craning so much I nearly come off the bike, spot a pair of green shoes. Two minutes later I'm crawling over the bricks and paint pots and old newspapers but probably not hypodermics, not in Hyde Vale. The pair of men's Birkenstocks look almost unworn. And Steve's boots are in tatters.

As the weather warms, find more things. A slim-fit Reiss shirt, draped on a hedge (drunk City boy stripping after the pub). A tiger-striped hoody. I feel bad about that because it looks fun, and leave it where it is for a day, only taking it when no one comes back for it. There's an element of Damaris Page's Rag Fair about all this, that industrious version of recycling where lost or bedraggled things got a new life instead of being left to rot. And with every item, I briefly take on a new character. For a while I'm someone else, and the clothes – sent by the fates, my open-air, all-natural wardrobe department – dictate the role.

✳

I've worn a lot of second-hand stuff before. There are reasons you'd think I wouldn't like it, the biggest being that, once we moved to the coast, Dad's family would drive down from Edmonton or Holloway for a day out and empty sacks of clothes they'd finished with onto the lumpy concrete patio for us to sort through. And we did. Even though some of those things smelled of sweat, or mould, or possibly urine. Maggie and me went through it enchanted, as if it was a dressing-up box, while Mum thanked the donors through her humiliation, her children thrilled by clothes Uncle Alf or Auntie Pat's family would otherwise burn. Cigarette in her mouth, Pat would hold one of her daughter Sheila's pleated Tricel dresses up against me. 'That'a do for a party, wunnit?' Yes! Even though there's lard on it.

I didn't always want to be who I became in those clothes. But the things I'm finding now are mysterious, and each, like me, is embarking on a new life.

✳

I could have stayed at the building society. I was making more than my dad got for mending roofs in driving rain while well-off old ladies came out to ask, 'Have you nearly finished? I can't hear the radio...'

There was more; I'd met my first real boyfriend, who worked at a building society down the road from mine. We were introduced on a training weekend in Eastbourne, when I was sitting in the bar in front of a Southern Comfort bought for me by the boyfriend of the girl whose room I shared so they could go up and shag. All around me, slaughtered trainee building society managers staggered to the beach, where they threw each other in the freezing sea. Paul wandered over and asked if I wanted my untouched drink. He couldn't think where he'd noticed me and I had to tell him; I had an account with the Woolwich, and three weeks ago I went into his branch, in my *duffel* coat, for a cheque to send with my UCCA form. Meanwhile, Paul had seen the Sex Pistols, the Clash and *Annie Hall*.

That was it. We started hitting gigs in his red Ford Capri – Generation X and Eddie and the Hot Rods at Hastings Pier Pavilion, Squeeze at London's Nashville Rooms, the Flying Pickets, Emmylou Harris and all her hair, the Mo-dettes. We saw mind-bending films at arthouse cinemas, and I started reading American fiction. He was cool for a building society bloke, and from a similar background to me – his dad a Polish caterer at Gatwick, his mum a police station typist. He spent our first Christmas at mine. Dad put a wallpaper table in the front room, since our kitchenette wasn't big enough, and he'd bought a bottle of red wine. 'We've had this in the fridge for hours, should be nice and cold.' He opened it, poured thimble-sized amounts into our tumblers, sipped his own and grimaced. 'Lovely stuff.'

Because of Paul, I was less sure about leaving for university. And in the end Exeter, full of public school kids, was a terrible mistake. On my course, there was Gub, whose home was a Banffshire castle and Chantal, who flew over each term from

Paris. I hung out with Jackie from Hounslow, the only other person from a comprehensive. We played pool and drank Guinness at the Red Cow, where few other students crossed the threshold and they had Magazine on the jukebox. When, in the second term, Jackie said she was quitting, I realised I'd come to the same conclusion. We didn't try hard enough to adapt, and we didn't really know how.

Paul came to collect me, my books, my vinyl and my record player one March Saturday. By now, he was assistant manager at Croydon Woolwich, with an unheated Victorian terrace in Thornton Heath, deposit paid by the sale of the Capri, and I moved in there. Next day, I went to Streatham Brook Street Bureau, did a typing test, had an interview – and instead of sending me after jobs, they suggested I could be an advisor. I found myself in an office in Tooting, where to use the loo you had to ask for a key, cross to a traffic island and let yourself in past the turnstile to the public toilets.

And then a golden ticket appeared: a vacancy came in for a letter answerer on *Woman's Weekly*. I told them I was sending the ideal candidate, then took an early lunch. Arriving at IPC, I stared up at the King's Reach building in sick fascination. They were all in there, journalists writing things, on *Woman* and *Honey* and *Anglers' Mail*. At the interview, I boasted about my typing speeds and the helpful letters I could write to readers.

As I opened the door at home, the phone was ringing.

I'd got it.

✳

A chancer who moved way faster than me was Elsa Lanchester. Do you know about her? She was born Elizabeth Sullivan at 48 Farley Road, Catford, on 28 October 1902, to bohemian – vegetarian – parents, members of the Social Democratic Federation who had creative hopes for her. Factory worker James 'Shamus' Sullivan, the son of a London

Irish policeman, taught himself bookkeeping and shorthand and got a job as a railway clerk. Suffragette Edith 'Biddy' Lanchester came from a family of architects. She turned her back on that to teach, was forced to leave because of her socialism and retrained as a secretary. When, at twenty-four, she told her parents she was moving in with her working-class partner in a 'free love union', her father and three of her brothers turned up at her lodgings, declared her demented and handcuffed her: for her own good, because what she intended was an act of 'social suicide'. They put her in an asylum, the cause of insanity logged as 'over-education'. After four days she was officially examined and found to be sane. She set up home with Sullivan and never saw her father again.

Elsa had her mother's mulishness and idealism. Biddy got her into a London boys' school, Mr Kettle's, where she played football and cricket. Desperate to be a classical dancer, at ten she won a scholarship to study in Paris with performance modernist Isadora Duncan, but Duncan was so snobbish and affected Elsa couldn't stand her. The school closed at the start of World War I and Elsa, eleven, was moved to a Hertford-shire boarding school away from London's bombing, where she taught dance in exchange for education and board. Back home at fourteen she gave local dance classes to bring in cash, at sixteen was hired by an Isle of Wight dance school, and at eighteen made her London debut as a music hall Egyptian dancer. She's larky, lively as a whippet. 'Come on, sir, up on stage. Too shy? Ah well, Pharoah enough.'

Then at twenty, she and her friend Harold Scott opened the scruffy Cave of Harmony, a dive bar club in Seven Dials which developed a reputation for 'Victorian cabaret'. Here in the Roaring Twenties, she's seen flappers and wants the creative freedom those middle-class girls have. And more.

What went on at the Cave is open to conjecture, but its vibe gives you an insight into Elsa, with her skyscraper forehead, dark eyes and lyrical voice. Though she and Scott performed one-act plays by Pirandello and Chekhov, she also delivered dirtily risqué music hall numbers. The club brought together slumming intellectuals like HG Wells, Aldous Huxley, Evelyn Waugh, film director James Whale. Here's a diary entry from novelist and playwright Arnold Bennett.

'Elsa Lanchester and Harold Scott came to lunch yesterday. She had a most charming dress, home-made; she said she had made it out of dusters. Very young. A lovely complexion, wonderful shock of copper hair; a rather queerly blunted nose. I offered to pay for some chairs and tables for the cabaret, but they were not keen, preferring the audience to sit on the floor. I should say these people are bound to do something good...'

So that's Arnold Bennett, an open-minded kind of man. And here's Vera Brittain, heroic but upper-class and offended:

'Clubs and societies existed where those believed to be specialists in the practices vaguely known as "vice" were welcome. The greater their interest in sodomy, lesbianism, pederasty and kindred topics was thought to be, the more welcome they were as associates. Radclyffe Hall frequented one club known as the Cave of Harmony, where Katherine Mansfield gave amateur stage performances... The locked-cupboard atmosphere of these places gave them their attraction.' You'd want a wash afterwards, perhaps?

The Cave didn't bring in much and, a blend of brassy and classy, Elsa was ready for anything to make enough to eat. She was a cleaner, a nude model, got paid to act as the 'other woman' so couples could get a divorce, and still appeared in revues. Whale remembered stage managing *Riverside Nights*, at the Lyric Hammersmith, where a beanpole in a top hat, tights and heels sang rude Cockney ballads. At the end she'd jump in a cab and tear across town to *The Midnight Follies*, changing in the back. Once her cab was stopped for speeding; naked, she calmly explained she was due onstage in five minutes. A rule-breaking free thinker, her reputation exploded. 'Art's a word that cloaks *oceans* of naughtiness,' she'd smile.

She began to find bit parts in movies, and closed the Cave of Harmony with a final few performances. There she is, slinking in through the smoke. She's joined by pudgy up-and-coming actor Charles Laughton. They croon 'Frankie and Johnny' like they mean it ('Frankie and Johnny were lovers/ Oh lordy how they could love...'). And they do. Less than a year later, they're married.

It's kind of inexplicable, because Laughton quickly becomes an enormous, misshapen slab. Yet he's erudite, lively, and adores her. They seem happy. Until two years later when he admits that he's gay, and he's just made love to a boy on the sofa of their London flat. Because she worships him, she doesn't shout or hit out. Torn between despair and compassion, she says the only thing she can, and it makes Laughton cry: 'It's all right. I understand.' After which she briefly becomes psychosomatically deaf, desperate not to have heard. She felt that in Laughton she had a true partner who cared the way she did about art, culture, even nature. Perhaps he might change. If he's happy to continue together, she says, so is she. 'But let's get rid of the sofa.'

It's Dad's birthday. Eighty-eight. I've sent a card. For years after I moved out he'd have little, often nothing, to do with me, because 1) he didn't like my immoral lifestyle; and 2) he couldn't be bothered because he hadn't wanted kids in the first place ('No man does, if they're honest.' He's not that close to Maggie either and she adores him). But since his showstopping heart op when I went to the Royal Brompton and apologised for, I'm not sure, being born, we've been on speakers and we do our best. I call the Devon semi in the afternoon to see what the day has so far held. 'Ooh, I got a nice card from Deirdre. Pair of socks and a packet of slim panatellas, which I shall save for special occasions. Picked it all myself, but don't tell her. And then she took me for a slap-up lunch in Wetherspoon's. Pint of beer, £1.75, big plates of steak and chips, and your stepmother had a glass of red wine.'

'Oh, really?'

'She always has that at twelve with her dinner. Lovely with an ice cube.'

✳

The problem is, Elsa became overwhelmed by Laughton. You think, driven, talented couple, will both go far, but no. Awed by his ability she put his career first and, as he became a great character actor, considered her own hopes second, or not at all. It's not even that he'd been poor, so her socialist principles made her want more for him. Three-quarters of her autobiography concentrates on his work. Once an irrepressible maverick, she fades from view. That *is* only while he's alive; but it's long enough.

In those years, she at least still acts a little in plays and movies, with him and solo. They perform Shakespeare, Wilde and Chekhov. Laughton gets contracts with Paramount and MGM, and they move to LA, where he mostly emotes (a menacing Dr Moreau in *Island of Lost Souls*, a heaving Captain Bligh in *Mutiny on the Bounty*, a very convincing Quasimodo) and she mostly climbs the Hollywood hills, picking wildflowers and admiring butterflies. Occasionally she'd turn up for an audition and not get the job because she'd introduced herself in her natural Cockney accent. She could have altered that, as she did when she performed, but often she was too irritated. For the most part, she endured Laughton's boyfriends (as a sensuous woman she had lovers too, though she wanted only Laughton), and protected his reputation by outwardly acting the happy and fulfilled wife.

Nineteen thirty-five. Lanchester is still only thirty-three. And James Whale, making his follow-up to *Frankenstein* and remembering her lively oddity, approaches her for the dual role of the monster's bride and Mary Wollstonecraft Shelley, Frankenstein's author. Most actresses wouldn't touch the jarringly scary role of the bride, but Elsa took it, and then had elocution lessons to perfect the clipped upper-class metre of Shelley (where she looks like a young Judy Garland). If you watch *Bride of Frankenstein*, or even Google the patchwork lady coming to life, then see Boris Karloff's Frankenstein meeting his betrothed, it's desperately moving. 'Friend?' asks the monster hopefully. And the bird-woman screams and hisses, a caw of fear when she sees her manmade husband. A tear rolls down his cheek. You'll never forget it. But I wonder now if that destroyed howl came from deeper in Lanchester, the lonely misery that love had brought her.

Actor and director Simon Callow, in his biography of Laughton, heaps abuse on Elsa. According to him, she stayed with Laughton for his influence, clinging to his coattails. Oh, for God's sake. Do you think Laughton would tolerate that, even for cover? Do you think the sort of idiosyncratic, opinionated woman Lanchester had been and still, beneath it all, remained would sell herself so short? She admired her husband, but for the most part it was mutual. Perhaps she still hoped he'd properly love her, the way he'd seemed to at the start. Only after his death did she tell another biographer of Laughton's sexuality. Asked why so frank, she said, 'Because times have changed. And because it might help people who are faced with the same kind of problem and must deal with the guilt that Charles felt most of his life.' A problem because they should really not have married. Perhaps if they'd never met, her spark might've blossomed.

But maybe it wouldn't. Working-class and proud of it, Elsa was offered too many Cockney charlady roles, and took them. She got a kick out of it, clutching mops and smudging her strange beauty with silly headscarves. And once Laughton had died, how did she spread her wings? By releasing albums of tongue-in-cheek music hall songs. Even before his death she'd begun to put on burlesque shows.

And clearly, her oceans of naughtiness still gushed deep. At the Turnabout on La Cienega Boulevard she'd sing the delightful 'When a Lady Has a Piazza' ('When a lady has a piazza/She has a prize indeed/She can look on her piazza/As a friend in need...'). Laughton thought it was tasteless, but when he saw the size of her audiences he relented, insisting on 'creating' and directing her show himself, and going nuts when she veered from what he'd set down. He became increasingly difficult, and on her first night at UCLA had a little hissy fit and tried to throw himself down the front steps, demanding pills to kill himself.

When he developed bone cancer, she began to be booked to replace him on his tour dates. 'It seemed fun for audiences to get my show instead of Charles',' she mused. 'Instead of readings of Shakespeare, they got a clown.'

I turn back to her as the bride again. Haunted, chiselled white face, cleft chin, furious black brows and pouting lips. Two lightning streaks of white running through her mass of hair. Body strapped in gimpy bandages, and over those a celestial wedding gown. Down her jaw and neck, the scar of

91

ragged stitches holding her together. James Whale, jilted by the only woman he loved and forever bitter (and subsequently homosexual), had decided this must be Mary Shelley's alter-ego because inside every woman was a bitch. Lanchester took that, smirked at him and ran with it, giving it a hypnotic otherness. I modelled my goth look entirely on her monster girl.

As Isadora Duncan told her dancers, 'You were wild once. Don't let them tame you.' Apart from Laughton, her Achilles' heel, Elsa never actually considered it.

✳

I couldn't crowbar myself into my background as Lanchester did. She united the riff-raff and the artist in herself, but I struggled at Dad's family get-togethers. His siblings and their children pulled out the stops at parties and weddings, blasting through a singalong – 'Come, come, come and make eyes at me/Dahn at the old Bull and Bush, la la la la laah.' Elsa would've loved it. I think. Although she never had to sit through it, and her salty songs were all delivered with a feminine *élan* and on her terms.

Dad's family didn't know what to do with Mum and her daffy innocence, or me and my sister. We didn't fit. God knows we tried, but we never got the innuendo, gazing at the gales of laughter where pork pies got dropped out of open mouths into pints of beer or spat helplessly across the table. Reading this now makes me grin, but we couldn't loosen up enough to join in, and Dad was ashamed: 'Get off yer 'igh 'orse.' High horse?? I felt like Sancho Panza on a mule.

Dad's arty, alcoholic dad was an exhibitionist too, playing violin sonatas for the family (uncle Harry, the only one I really liked, was shocked that those made him cry). But Mum's lot, the De la Moules, were genuine show people. Bewitching auntie Joy was the naughty trapeze artiste, and there were photographs of Mum as a girl, doing the splits in a man's suit and top hat. Her brother had a swing band and played piano, though Dad was less than flattering about Frank's vibraphone skills.

My sister grabbed the dramatic baton with both hands, Elsa invented herself, but I'm still lumbered with a reading of the world I don't much like, playing a part – aged grouch and complainer – that I actually hate. As I should've guessed back at FE in Chichester, you can't work out the part you want to play in life til you've lived, at least a bit. You've got to try role after role, observe the parts other women give themselves. As you get older parts stay in place longer, probably even failing ones, because you've got less energy. And life sticks its oar in, changing you despite yourself.

Someone nudges the door with a foot and Elsa Lanchester in middle age appears, clutching mugs of builders' tea. She drags over my spare chair, sits down, crosses her legs. 'Can I ask, what happened to putting the negativity in the bin, like you started doing two weeks ago, or replacing it with daisies? Your mother was a cleaner, I've played chars, it's not as if, between us, we haven't shown you how to tidy.'

I've been trying quite hard to be positive.

'But you sink back repeatedly into this mournful stewing. Why?'

Habit. Comfort. Blimey, this tea's horrible.

Her foot taps. 'Here's an idea. Could the trepidation be excitement?'

Are you mad?

'Turn that adrenaline into anticipation. You do it with feature writing.'

More so in the past. I was stretchy. Didn't have a fifty-something brain.

'Well, you've got one now, use it before it seizes up. Instead of panic, why not shiver with how you'll tackle the day. What direction could you take it in?'

Cul-de-sac? Off a cliff?

'I don't have to bother. This is your final warning. We've all done our best, but you've got other issues to tackle. And you're developing whimper lines in your chin. Get it or forget it.'

Tough *love*. And the chair's empty. Briefly watch a YouTube clip of her being interviewed by Dick Cavett in her seventies, having fun, flirting with her host. She endured huge disappointments, including several abortions, the last so botched she couldn't have children at all. One of these was Laughton's child. Why would she get rid of it? Did he request that? If he did, wouldn't it break her heart? And yet asked about her marriage she said, 'I remember more of the happy times and block out the sad ones.'

Maggie does that. Years ago, we're standing by a bus stop near her home. Grey and wet, Scotland. Her son's tiny, husband's in a mood. And she starts to sing 'There's No Business like Show Business'. Whaaat? But the tension lifts, so I join in. 'Nowhere do you get that happy feeling/When you are stealing that extra bow!' Boy starts giggling, husband grins. Steve is stunned and thinks we've rehearsed. 'There's no people like show people/They smile when they are low...'

By the end we're punching the air.

Go on with the show. Because okay, they say you won't go far, but then something works out and boom! Next day on your dressing room, a star.

Those albums of Lanchester's. *Bride of Frankenstein Sings Bawdy Cockney Songs*, that's one. Featuring 'If You Peek in my Gazebo', 'Fiji Fanny' and the incomparable 'If You Can't Get in the Corners'. The picture on the sleeve shows her, hair flying, laughing in a negligee.

That's what she chose. I've been like that, so let's just say we'll do this whenever it's possible. If I wake up tense one final thing I'll try is taking the day's project, and mood, in a brighter – even subtly daring – new direction, and I'll start by humming as I feed the cats. Maybe something like 'My New York Slip', from *Songs for a Shuttered Parlor.*

'My Boston slip was fancier and cost a great deal more/ My San Francisco slip was, confidentially, a booore.../My Texas slip was pleasant but impractical at best/As were most of the rest. But my New York slip!' Others are overrated but this one's *never* dated, and I still am fascinated by my New York fling, or in fact this airy aspect of myself that I can, if I adjust my mind, whip out of the wardrobe and put on, even for one key minute.

✳

Meanwhile, I found myself at *Woman's Weekly,* writing to customers whose special offer fuchsias had arrived bedraggled or who'd got a springtime dress with a popper missing. That was okay. I'd smuggled myself inside the holy walls. I was steps from journalists and I was gonna be one.

7

Write back atcha

The plot of your life should have beautiful twists.
Which might need more planning than you've given it

I said I don't want a smear test, thanks, or not without a full anaesthetic. Plus I've got a retroverted uterus, even the most experienced gynaecologist struggles. It can go on forever once they crank up that speculum and start hunting round, the trembling jaws desperate to snap shut inside you. 'Try to relax. You're making it harder by being tense.' Speculum. A 19th-century instrument designed by men, that we still use.

But this is the lovely Chinese doctor. Everything had been going so well. I've had an ultrasound. I've had my blood test. She said, 'You look much better. More relaxed?' and I said, yes, I was making a conscious effort to let go. And how was it, having stopped HRT? No pain with sex? Oh... not so you'd notice.

She smiled. You've taken real responsibility for your health. And just to check, how often are you getting up for a pee in the night now? I said, about twenty times?

Which is how I'm up on the bed. Anyone else, forget it, but Doctor Tranh is the business. Only first, can't get the speculum in. 'You're very dry.' Then can't really see anything. And then... High five! It is! Vaginal atrophy!

Apparently coming off HRT has made things dryer, and the walls are paper-thin. Also, though she doesn't say it, atrophy can happen to things that don't get used. I feel like I want to take out my tired, emotional vagina and give it some TLC. Put it to bed with a hot water bottle, read it a story.

But it wouldn't like that. What it wants is this special cream, which has synthetic oestrogen like a mild HRT and... oh, who cares? That evening, lie on the bathroom floor and put the tiny plunger inside myself. Glance to the side. I don't think I've seen the bathroom from this angle. God, this floor is *filthy*.

Anyway, it's not a deal. 'Atrophy': waste away, shrivel. Now I've turned a certain corner, the well of shame I can accommodate is bottomless. Still, in the night a gurgling sound wakes me. Finally locate the source. It's Florence, ginger warrior and feline alter ego. That's my girl. Throwing up all over the vaginal atrophy leaflet.

＊

No one in my family was a writer, but someone wanted to be, and that was Dad. He had virtually no education, signing up during the war at fifteen, but his efforts when I was ten or eleven to write for the *Reader's Digest* are etched on my brain. The *Digest* liked dramatic real-life stories, such as getting wedged in a crevasse on the Matterhorn or being trapped while a shark is coming and having to cut your arm off with a penknife. Horrifically, maybe because I was all right at English, Dad gave me the first of his pieces to read before he sent it off. It was about a medical procedure where a catheter was inserted into his bladder via his willy, and his insurmountable agony. I read in acute embarrassment. Dad had poured his heart out but the feature came back; about a year later, like they'd just found it behind the radiator.

He kept trying for months, different medical tales. I didn't know he'd had so much wrong, maybe it was all that dripping. Anyway, then he stopped. We weren't allowed in Mum and Dad's bedroom but I can only imagine a manila envelope somewhere full of rejections – Dad's effort to change his life and not end up where he is now, an old bloke who can only look at his tools because his hands are gnarled with rheumatoid arthritis. So it's all very charming for me to say you can reinvent your role in the world; sometimes the fight takes more than you can give.

✳

At eleven, I'd been trying to make up 'stories' for ages. Even plays. I was devastated when, at five, having just learned to write and scrawled a page of my first play, Dad said me, him and Mum couldn't perform it by reading from one sheet. We needed our own copies. I wrote it out three times and the effort nearly broke me. I think it lost something in translation because once we started, Dad got hysterics at the name of Mum's character. 'Belly?'

'It's Belle, Dad.'

But he wasn't having it. Mum, struggling with my writing, said her line, then Dad guffawed, 'But no one can help you, Belly!' My play was probably so brief, let alone devoid of plot, that Dad was trying to provide some light relief, but after a few more interjections, I threw down my script and stormed off. That was the end of plays. Stories, then features, could be wrestled and fought to the ground in private.

✳

I wasn't on *Woman's Weekly* for long. I sat with three fiftysomething secretaries, all of us members of the National Society of Operative Printers and Assistants, a union fuelled by seething resentment. I hated even the word Natsopa, like some weird washing powder, and longed for the celestial circles of the NUJ, though conversation amongst the ladies revolved around elevenses, teatime biscuits and how hilarious and stupid journalists were. Every lunchtime I was down in the podium scanning the vacancy boards. What could I do? Openings for fashion writers. Knitting editors. Caravan correspondents. The music magazines – *NME, Melody Maker* – looked incendiary, a rebel Sistine Chapel. And then there was a job as sub-editor on bulky monthly *Woman & Home*. I applied, had an interview, did a test, and when they said I'd

98

got it, nearly collapsed. 'You can go next week,' snarled my office manager, 'if this job's not good enough.'

Four days later I had an NUJ card.

I thought I was going to cry.

It's time to look at the female writers now, the pioneers, and I'm intimidated. These three – Aphra Behn, Eliza Haywood, Abigail Scott Duniway – were ridiculed and attacked and didn't give an inch, they fought to write and make money from it, which God knows still isn't easy. And they wrote well, though men said they didn't because their work differed from the things men had to say, which were the things of interest. I've picked this trio because one was the first British female to write for money, and because among the handful of women who wrote, these three were working-class. And I'm happy to say they were good-looking, sophisticated and droll, so put that in your pipe, Georgian and Victorian critics who insisted they were harridans. Christ, they're coming up the stairs. I can hear skirts rustling, the clump of square heels... Okay, they're not seeing anything I've written.

'She has this entire room for her work?' Excuse me, Ms Haywood, I'm actually here. 'What are these boxes? "Cuttings". For plants? Ah, keepsakes, and dispatches to prompt ideas, for new work to bloom? I have something similar.'

'And she stores clothes in this room, too.' Aphra Behn, drily observant. 'A cat inside this wardrobe. Here, puss.'

'But on the desk – her writing machine?' Gently mocking laughter. 'Bigger than a mangle. How very much neater is the quill.'

'Or indeed,' Scott Duniway's Illinois drawl, 'my pint-sized iron horse of a typewriter. Noisy, sure. But I see daylight all around me. The sun is not blotted out by a large grey board.'

Never saw my iMac that way – space to arrange things, room to splash about. Still, natural light *is* virtually obliterated.

'Also, I like to pound things when I'm angry. For this, typewriting is excellent.'

'All women together ought to let flowers fall upon the tomb of Aphra Behn... for it was she who earned them the right to speak their minds. It is she – shady and amorous as she was – who makes it not quite fantastic for me to say to you tonight: Earn five hundred a year by your wits.'

You might know the Virginia Woolf quote from *A Room of One's Own*. (Though did you read the rest, where Woolf belittles Behn's talents as hackery because she had to write for money? Virginia, you snob.) But Behn: first professional woman writer in English literature, born 1640, died at forty-eight. Look at her, in that 1873 sketch by George Scharf, an open-minded man for a Victorian, from a portrait that's been lost. Tumbling hair, low décolletage, frank glance. No jewellery. She could be a shadowy Batcave club queen. Though even here, her eyes are puffy. She drove herself hard.

Behn's background is shrouded in mystery, probably her own doing (she invented things to make herself look saleable, and was also a talented spy). Hunting for information, her biographer Janet Todd despairs: 'She is not so much a woman to be unmasked as an unending combination of masks'. Still, it's generally agreed she was born in Harbledown near Canterbury, to barber Bartholomew Johnson and Elizabeth Denham, a wet nurse. There's a baptism dated 14 December in the parish register, when the baby was known as Eafry. The civil war was brewing.

How does a kid from a straw-floored hovel become a playwright and punk poetess? First, you learn to read. One of her mother's charges (wet-nursing could go on for years) was top-drawer Thomas Colepeper. It's likely Aphra accompanied Elizabeth to the stately house and found and begged to be helped with books, perhaps getting taught by the family's governess alongside Thomas and his sister. Wealthy families could often be amused by pretty, dirt-poor little girls, and would welcome them as companions for their daughters, though they lost interest as the child grew up, ushering it back to the gutter. But if she'd wriggled into this world, with its access to knowledge and fascinating vocabulary, Behn wasn't the type to abandon it without a fight.

It was useful too that Bartholomew's barber shop was in Canterbury, where trade included French Huguenots and Dutch refugees who'd come through Dover. Playing a flageolet to entertain waiting clients, little Aphra might well learn bits of French and Dutch there. *'Salut, messieurs! Écoutez.'*

But now the trail goes cold, for years. All we can do, hunting through various scraps, is press on and go with what feels most right.

So. Thomas Colepeper grew into an eccentric man obsessed with class, but it didn't stop him being genuinely fond of his plebby 'foster sister' Eafry; she was, he'd later boast, 'a most beautifull woman, and most Excellent Poet'. While they were young, he might well have introduced her – a tawny-skinned girl with a brain like a planet – to his aristocratic cousins, young earls and dukes who would talk to her about philosophy and literature. Aphra grabbed it gratefully. Did her dad, like mine, laugh at her work? She seems dismissive about fathers in her writings, was an 'insubordinate' child and hilariously had been earmarked for a nun. Obviously she's after a way out.

Charles II was barely ensconced before Colepeper had a job at court; by his side, the now cultured Eafry, or Eaffrey, or Afra. Colepeper was highly regarded, having campaigned for Charles before the Restoration, and was likely involved with the intelligence service. He recruited Aphra as a spy.

Some think, though the whole thing sounds insane, that at twenty-three our heroine – plus her family, because a single woman who's not a slut can't travel unaccompanied – is sent to the English colony of Surinam in the West Indies, an informer for the King on its corrupt administration. Really? Well, maybe. Because twenty years later Aphra will write a shocking novel set in Surinam: *Oroonoko*. She could have based it on reports about the place, but if she'd never been, it seems odd she'd be so fervent. The story plunges into desire, politics, rebellion and brutal punishment as African prince Oroonoko is tricked into slavery. It sold well, fell into obscurity and has been reclaimed as the breakthrough it was. Behn said most of her work was based on real life, sometimes her own, and many think *Oroonoko* fictionalises true events. In which case, she's writing faction, a form not tried before.

Anyway, listen to this. Surinam was a melting pot, Africans, English, Dutch. Next thing, Behn's back in London, 'And I'm married, handily, to Dutch merchant Johann Behn, *dank je wel.*' Marrying means she's recognised as a person, which a single woman could only barely claim to be, and free of her

102

dad's control, though she'd be subject to her husband's. But look, Johann's died. Disappeared entirely. If he existed. See what she did there? A masterstroke. Aphra, twenty-five, with the status of a widow and no husband to obey. If you were a woman who wanted independence, you couldn't make it up. Or you could: no documents have been found to confirm any marriage. My guess on this can't be right, because why wouldn't other women do the same thing? Ah, but most wanted actual husbands.

Needing money, she may at this point have done copying work. Newsletters and poems were in demand, and so was a good-looking copying girl, who sometimes helped a gentleman with other things. Girl copyists sharpened their own goose or raven quills, licked a quill clean when it got greasy, ruled lines and rubbed them out with bread once the letters were dry. Her writing got speedier.

Then she made a mistake, and not in a letter. Courtier and dramatist Thomas Killigrew suggested she'd make a fine spy in the Anglo-Dutch war, and at twenty-six she was off again, to Antwerp. Her codenames were Agent 160, Mrs Bean (nooooo) and Astrea – literally 'star-maiden', and the Greek goddess of innocence and purity. Except that while 1666 saw plague and fire rip London to pieces, Aphra was in Belgium trying to keep her psyche whole as she used sex to buy secrets.

She arrived in Bruges with a to-do list that included gathering information on the Dutch fleets and luring an agent back to the English side. Letters she wrote let you hear the voice of a girl struggling in a swamp of intrigue.

And Killigrew wasn't paying her. On Boxing Day 1666, she pleaded for funds. She'd warned the Home Office about the Dutch intention to attack the British fleet on the Thames but her warning was dismissed, the Dutch burned ships, and her mission was a failure. Borrowing £150, she got home. Still no payment. Why? Was she the only working-class person employed by the intelligence service, didn't they see when she said she needed money, she meant it? Threatened with debtors' prison, her last letter to Killigrew was blotched with tears. 'Sir, if you could guess at the affliction of my soule you would I am sure Pity me... I have cryed myself dead. Oh god, this is my reward for all my great promises, and my endeavors?' The money came eventually and when it did, she was twenty-eight and determined never to let anything like this happen again. Who can you trust? *Only* yourself.

✳

Sit back from the screen, where I'm craning forward, and let go of my shoulders, which have relocated themselves somewhere up round my ears. Okay, I've been feeling you reading behind me, Aphra. Is this how you'd write it? Frown at her, steps away by my bookshelves, where the inventor of painstaking research mixed with imagination is unconvincingly squinting and running her finger along the spines. Come on, talk to me. She glances round. 'Possibly. I wouldn't show Aphra Behn to be a stupid child.'

That's not what I'm doing.

The American voice interrupts. 'Can't be objective if it's about yourself. It's her thing, not ours, she must wrangle it through. Find a way to make it work, as we did.'

Aphra grunts a laugh. 'What, as in *No one can help you, Belly?*'

How humiliating.

'No, not like that. By the way, have you tried those cookies in the kitchen?'

The Rich Tea biscuits?

'Wholesome. Oaty and sweet, with cocoa nibs.'

The *Tracker* bars?

✳

Perhaps Killigrew felt some guilt. London was rebuilding, theatres were full. Director of the King's Company, he recruited Aphra to copy out scripts and maybe even adapt old plays, giving them current appeal.

As she modernised the phrasing, she analysed these plays. Some were bloody awful. As for the playwrights and poets – well, John Dryden, all politics until Nell Gwyn appears and he finally writes something funny. Andrew Marvell, so desperate to get it on, and John Donne, thirty years dead but actually a louche inspiration. Humour and sex mattered, and where were the women writing about them? She drummed inky fingers. 'All right. One, I need to generate income, not simply beg for copying. And two, I doubt myself often, but I could write. I know it.'

Revolutionary. During the seventeenth century, less than one per cent of all texts published were by women, and apart from Behn these women were aristocrats, with leisure and every opportunity to pay for their work to appear.

Filled with ambition, Behn wrote like the wind – over the next decade nineteen of her plays, starting with *The Forc'd Marriage* when she's thirty, were staged. No one knows how she broke in, but she did. There she is at her desk, furiously stomping old quills to the floor and sharpening new ones. Standing up to stride about, reading aloud what she's written and laughing her head off as she thinks of the next, funnier or more devastatingly candid scene. She must have gone nuts with relief when the first cheque came in. In the preface to her play *Sir Patient Fancy*, she describes herself as 'Forced to write for bread and not ashamed to owne it'.

Clever, rude, revealing, Behn's plays starred prostitutes and scoundrels, and burned with mischief and outrageous repartee. She herself had lovers, probably male and female, as was the way then (certainly for men). In her unique position, living like a female Shakespeare in her garret, she became a bohemian libertine. It's incredible. Did she stroll into taverns and drink with male playwrights – 'Good evening, fine fellows, even those of you on the floor. Written anything decent lately?' - despite their ingrained prejudice? Did she flirt and seduce, snog men in corners, invite them back to hers for her famous milk punch (milk with whisky, rum and syrup) and a tumble, then smile, 'Now get lost'? In my mind she's Madonna in her heyday. Her plays are populist but their themes are original, and people queue to see them, which is the aim. *Oroonoko* probably was the first anti-slavery piece, moving in its scrutiny of the hero's thoughts. Only Shakespeare had given a black hero this much attention before.

But Aphra was shackled too, in a way. First by the writing, the new role. She was at the playhouse early, day after day, putting actors through their paces, furious when they didn't learn their lines. But something nastier controlled her. She lived what she wrote about, wrote what she lived, and one character, courtesan Angellica Bianca from her play *The Rover*, makes you sit up. Angellica is clever, and financially and sexually independent as a man. But she falls for Willmore, based maybe on the King; maybe on Behn's friend John Wilmot, the debonair, syphilitic earl of Rochester; but most likely on John Hoyle, a promiscuous piece of work (a lawyer, by the way) with whom Behn was involved in a tortured affair and with whom, at the time of *The Rover*, she'd been obsessed for seven years. Willmore, like Hoyle, was devastatingly magnetic. The sexual tension ripples off the stage.

Angellica's speech, when she finds that the man she saw as her partner - dangerous, but hers - has chosen to marry a young aristocrat, is the sound of a woman imploding.

'What have you, sir, to say? Nay, do not speak, for I know well if I should hear thee out, thou'd talk away all that is brave about me. Alas. I thought all men were born to be my slaves, and held my power like lightning in my eyes. But when love held the mirror, that cruel glass reflected all the weakness of my soul. My pride turned to a submissive passion. And so I

106

bowed – which I ne'er had done before. I thought that I had won you, that you would value me the higher for my folly. But now, I see you made me... your spaniel bitch. Why did'st thou give me oaths? Why kneel and make me soft? Why did'st thou *enslave* me?'

Could you write a speech like that without feeling it?

The Rover's first performance was in 1677, the year Behn's relationship with Hoyle was at its bleakest. As Angellica, Aphra can howl her heartbreak and fury to the world.

(How did this creep, by the way, do what he did? Jack Hoyle was vain, sadistic, some think latently gay, an aspect that may have appealed to Aphra, a very fluid masculinity when she also liked women. More interested in finding a challenging female to dismantle than in sex – maybe not even capable: Behn writes repeatedly of male impotence in the face of female desire – Hoyle surrounded himself with other manipulators, men and women, flirting in front of her. She suggested a break but found herself stalking him, watching from a distance. Finally she got a grip, pouring herself into work, giving her female characters the power she wished she had.)

Perhaps Behn married (again), this time for love, but I doubt it. She may have had children, but there's no evidence. Though in her prime she strode across the page grinning like the Cheshire Cat, I don't actually see contentment.

But that's not what she set out to find! A prankster, a sly comic, she had a huge gang of friends, met Nell Gwyn and formed a bond, two working-class girls soaring, and the pair were endlessly involved in bonkers practical jokes.

To the end, Behn still wrote for anyone, in virtually any form – translating, more copying, political pamphlets that are virtually marketing – because half the time she was destitute. At around forty-four, her health began to fail. Writer's cramp became arthritis that twisted her hands into talons. Everyone knew she wasn't well; at forty-six, an attack appeared by now-forgotten satirist Tom Brown, discussing 'that lewd harlot, that Poetick Quean/Fam'd through White Fryars, you know who I mean...' It snorted that 'long with a Sciatica, she's beside lame, Her limbs distortur'd, Nerves shrunk up with pain...' She must've longed to rest – she said she did – but she crashed on, depressed, overworked, her tangled curls grey as Margaret Atwood's. And still she died in poverty, in debt despite all her efforts.

That's partly because fashion changed, Behn's racy writing and the adventurous roles of her women were condemned, and she dropped out of favour. There was always someone to denounce her differentness. Many women hated her for writing the sort of thing they only covertly enjoyed from a man. The hypocrisy made her spit. As she scribbled in her preface to *Sir Patient Fancy*: 'I printed this play with all the impatient haste one ought to do, who could be vindicated from the most unjust and silly aspersion Woman could invent to cast on Woman: that it was Baudy, the least and most Excusable fault in the Men writers to whose Plays they all crowd.'

✳

Rub my cheek. Well, she's a smudged goddess. It sickens me that she died with her aching hands wrapped in bandages to keep them warm. Didn't you, Aphra? She rolls her eyes, twisted paws thrust up inside her sleeves.

And I can't forget the longing in a sentence she wrote a year before she died, thinking about: '...that perfect Tranquillity of Life, which is nowhere to be found but in retreat, a faithful Friend and a good Library'.

Well, she never got tranquillity. But if she hadn't been poor, maybe there wouldn't have been the pressure to use her imagination and get on with it the way she did. While a handful of posh ladies were writing a little, then strolling in the grounds, fired-up Eaffrey Johnson was punching out plays, some dull, some wonderful, lighting a new candle from the last one, frowning and berating herself, or nodding her head – 'Yes. That *is* what happens...'; her only and fiercest champion. She had to scrabble like a dog but, for a time, she had a fulfilment and delight those women would never know.

*

Walk over to her and put my hand against hers – yours, Aphra – palm to palm, your right against my left, our writing hands. Peer into your face, as if we're on either side of Alice's looking-glass.

'Hoyle. Oh, I wanted him the minute I saw him,' you say. 'What would you do? Well, you've done the same. But really? I'm glad it didn't last. He stifled me – not wanting me, just jealous of the writing. My confidence had begun to shrivel. If I'd had him, I'd be a miserable, insecure woman who never wrote *The Rover* or *Oroonoko* and didn't even try.'

The wardrobe door is ajar, and you focus briefly on a couple of the skirts there. 'Better than what you have on. Don't you wear these?'

Not at the moment. Anyway...

'Anyway. I didn't want to fuck him. He was terrible at it.' You think for a minute. 'Actually, yes. Awful.' Snort of laughter. 'Girls were better. So I don't know what he had, but it wasn't that. He was just my problem. No, *I* was my problem. And after me, him.'

The grit that makes the pearl.

8

Woman & Home was a delightful magazine. I proof-read galleys and fitted other journalists' work. The subs' room was silent; you could hear the clock tick. I stayed there too long, partly because my giggly mum died suddenly of a brain tumour when I was twenty-two, and I lost my drive.

She'd had wipe-out, throwing-up headaches for years. Our doctor sighed, 'You're neurotic, Mrs Brown. Take an aspirin.' So she did and, white-faced, carried on cleaning classroom floors, dragging her bucket and mop around, retrieving and lining up chalk by the blackboards. Aspirins didn't work that well on a growth which, having had years to hone its talents, killed her over a weekend so no one had a chance to say good-bye. I was in Yorkshire, on holiday with Paul. Maggie, fifteen, was in Leicester at a school dance project. Mum was forty-eight. Dad had to find Maggie and me and tell us. I moved back and tried to be a shadow mum, delivering midday Findus Crispy Pancakes then watching Dad head off to work with his roof-rack of ladders and Maggie walk silently to school. The funeral director came for his cheque, which we couldn't afford.

The September day of Mum's funeral was warm and sunny. There were bouquets from her friends and neighbours. She could never afford flowers, if only she could've had just one of these. Stepping outside the crematorium, the flowers were spread on the grass, and it seemed for a moment every-thing was light, as if Mum was surrounding us. Lightness was her thing. Like the day I dropped in to see her at work after college. Her face lit up, she put a finger to her lips and said, 'Come and see this.' We walked down the corridor that reeked of polish to another classroom, where, in a big tray, under warm lights, chicks were hatching. Some were asleep but some were awake, stumbling about, and the sound, the cheeping, soft and warbling... And Mum's young face, which I can hardly remember even when I struggle, and her hand holding mine. I don't know why I'm crying now, it's lightness.

✳

I developed eczema and asthma after that and when I got ringworm from scratching the eczema, I had to spend weeks at home and started writing again, just for me. At work, I'd tried to write features for the magazine, but I could never have written for *Woman & Home*; they wanted stuff about flower arranging or Luciano Pavarotti. Instead, I got a few tiny pieces with *Number One*, a B-list *Smash Hits*. And then I heard about a subbing vacancy on headbanging rock weekly *Racket*.

The office was a freezing dump above Edgware Road tube station, rattling all day with train noise. The editor seemed to be a PCP-addicted pimp and the staff looked like some kind of malevolent *Muppet Show*; a pack of punks, failed goths and two heavy metallers. Willie, the features editor from Leith, was emaciated due to his heroin habit. Of the two female journalists, one (the reviews editor) was a bloated upper-middle-class alcoholic and the other, a sub who was shagging the editor, had orange hair, an attitude, and kept snakes. I got the job because, I think I'm right in saying, no one else applied.

I was on a music paper! This would be awesome. Except the staff couldn't believe how straight I was, plus I worked too hard. I kept my desk neat, not strewn with flyers, old socks, stray bras, smashed bits of 45s used as coasters and half-empty beer bottles; a band once sent us all individual Jiffy bags of dog crap after an unfavourable review, but not even the art editor hung on to that. I sat opposite the lovely Willie, and he was the kindest person in the place. I got him teas, coffees, light refreshments, even the Dime bar that broke his tooth,

111

though all his teeth were jumping ship. I swished his dandruff off our shared phone with a press release, handed him a promo T-shirt when he sweated through his own – once he was on methadone he was wringing wet all day – and disposed of the evidence when he was sick in our waste bin. Once, when I took off my glasses while making a point about The Bangles ('I'm not sure you can call this piece "Wrist Job"...'), he smiled raggedly, 'Aw Miss Broon, you're byootifuw.' I adored him then.

I nagged and nagged to write for *Racket* and in the end they gave in, because it would be copy they didn't have to pay a freelance for. I interviewed a young French pseudo-jazz singer. Stu, the deputy editor, said, 'Erm, that feature. Actually it's not bad. Can you do some more?'

Try to stop me. I interviewed The Fuzztones, deafening psychotropic cowboys, and The Men They Couldn't Hang, and tripped-out Head at Soho boozer the Spice of Life. Asking such chronically naïve questions they probably thought I had some stitch-up act going, but when they realized I was hanging on their every word they relaxed and said more, assuming I was too dim to use it, but I did use it, not initially grasping what I had. A sweet rockabilly with a lariat tie and quiff, I did the singles, dragging home bags of 45s on the bus in my hobble skirt. Mister Bluebird on my shoulder.

✳

There is a student somewhere in the States with a tattoo of Elizabeth Haywood on her arm. That's how ground-breaking Haywood, and the student, are. Haywood's so able that embittered poet Alexander Pope (picture Jeremy Paxman crossed with a pike) has a vicious go at her in a satirical verse. Haywood wins because she has a good life, and though it holds sadness and loss, it's full and joyous too. Most of it.

She's probably born in 1693, daughter of a London stock-ingmaker called Fowler. Facts are surprisingly vague, when you realise she burst like a rocket on the literary scene with her first book, *Love In Excess*, an instant best-seller. For a while she just writes erotic bodice-rippers, partly because that's what she likes and partly because she needs cash and being an early Jackie Collins is one way to get it.

Pope got all worked up about her 'most scandalous books', but what really upset him is that Eliza had put his BFF's nose out of joint, and then triumphed over adversity. She probably had a baby with this friend, poet Richard Savage, who seduced then left her. A cross between a young Emma Thompson and a young Kate Winslet, and an equal mix of sense and sensibility, Eliza eventually began an open, very contented live-in relationship with bookseller and actor William Hatchett, with whom (it's probably him) she'd have a second child.

What's interesting is that Richard Savage can't stop writing about her. While they're together, as a sphinxy stunner; a few years later, when she's annoyingly happy with Hatchett, as a 'haggar'd shrew'. Where he used to praise her work, now he says she can only do it with a man's help; she's a sad 'Printer's Drudge' with no ideas of her own. If Savage only had a Twitter account more people might've read his mental troll-prints.

He was wrong. Haywood's early novels – a new form of writing, but one she helped establish just by doing it – might be sex romps, but they talked about women having desires and how those weren't accepted. Her work gradually focused on women's rights. By mid-career, her heroines were being locked up or otherwise tormented by domineering men and, unlike the future heroines of, say, Emily Brontë, they didn't find that exciting. Near the end of her writing life, long-term commitment is described as delightful. Here, I'm sure Hatchett *was* an inspiration.

Let's have a look at *Love In Excess*. It's whip-cracking chick lit about the escapades of Count D'Elmont, a rake of the worst sort who matures and becomes a lovely human being. So it's a rom-com fairy story, but it holds out hope that these things can happen – some distance from Aphra Behn's dark finales. The book is littered with free-thinking females: horny girls who demand a good time, get one, then find lasting contentment (quite wrong in the 1700s). The book went through multiple reprints, not one of which Haywood was paid for because at that time there were no royalties.

A couple of books further on, she kicks out the jams with *Fantomina: or Love in a Maze,* which stars an upper-class girl who anonymously acts out the roles of prostitute, maid, widow and lady of leisure to repeatedly seduce Mister Beauplaisir. She gets banished to a nunnery in the end but arguably that's a nice rest. Another bonkbuster. Sells buckets.

There are one or two exploitative low points, but Haywood's prolific. Like Behn, she needs to sell her writing for income, particularly when she has children. She'll eventually have Hatchett though, and he must meet her halfway financially because she's able to leave behind big-selling sleaze and, still driven at fifty-eight, publish *The History of Miss Betsy Thoughtless*, the first English novel where a woman's psychological development is clearly charted. Betsy's clever but at the start a stupid flirt (so the name), alienating a good man, Trueworth, by refusing to take marriage seriously. She marries a bully, finds the guts to leave him and there's an astonishing period of happy, enlightened independence. When she encounters Trueworth again, she finds taking on the female role in a union between two decent people can be unexpectedly pleasurable. The book's been seen as a forerunner to Charlotte Brontë's *Jane Eyre*, even to Austen.

How did Haywood even start writing? At first, she's desperate to act, something her family don't like. At twenty-one she somehow gets a place at Dublin's Smock Alley Theatre, a respected training ground, where she registers as a widow. She actually did marry, at seventeen, though it's not clear who Mister Haywood was. He probably didn't like her acting either, but she must've taught herself to perform, and either he dies, or she does a bunk.

At twenty-four she transfers to a theatre at Lincoln's Inn Fields. And has just one part in five years. Why? The theatre's director-producer John Rich has seen something in her: real potential for words and stories. He asks her to rewrite a failing play, and it's a stormer. She concentrates on rewriting, attempting her own work in secret. Two years later we get *Love in Excess*, and suddenly everybody knows her name. At thirty, she delivers her first original play, about a miser pimping out his wife, with a theme of supportive sisterhood. Madly successful.

✳

I got the gossip page 'editorship' when the guy who'd been its editor (Don, with an overbite and an S&M club) was promoted to news. Laying it out on massive sheets of semi-transparent paper was like grappling with an albatross, and it was hard to concentrate with Einstürzende Neubauten and The Butthole Surfers blaring from the record deck. Because nothing I commissioned ever fitted I started writing sections myself. Infatuated with one of the freelances, a louche, hyper-intelligent *Lost Boys* type, and increasingly fixated by the sort of music Paul dismissed, doomy, sexy, poetic goth, I began to change my look, turning into Lily Munster. I gave myself a column in my alter-ego's name: Morticia Wax. It got sacks of hate mail, but even that didn't make the staff like me.

And then we got a new editor, from *NME*. He was faced with open hostility from the troops, who saw his previous paper as a cabal of prancing public schoolboys. But this chap wanted me to write more. I did a major interview, Morrissey. I talked to The Cure's Robert Smith, who insisted we chat sitting on a traffic island opposite his Maida Vale local, where he was *totally* inconspicuous. On tour with The Cult in Texas, me and the photographer got free drinks at every venue because Texas thought I was Kate Bush. And I had an au-dience with Nick Cave, the dark lord, in Berlin. We wound up at a lock-in near the East German border so everyone could watch the World Cup final. Around midnight, I couldn't take much more. The PR was running a book on the result, standing on a table fighting off punters. Cave was comatose on a bench seat. I got past the security dude and looked around outside. Deserted, Cold War streets in every direction. So I just had to go back in again.

I couldn't believe I was being paid to do this. But then I made a mistake. Willie was sacked: he'd gone to sleep under his desk one too many times. I applied for his job – and I got it. Sometimes, even when you just think the words 'poi-soned chalice', you can see the thing in front of you, smoking.

✳

It's got to be Haywood's freewheeling personal life that fed into the risqué books she'd been writing. When that first original play is put on, a play by another writer appears too: in you come, minor poet Richard Savage. Haywood throws sense to the wind and the following year has a baby with him, though he seems unbalanced. When their child is a year old, the couple separate, possibly because the hard-up Savage transfers his affections to rich girl would-be writer Martha Sansom. It's when Eliza finds a better love that Savage goes crazy and his pal Alexander Pope begins his attack.

It appears in 1728, when Haywood, thirty-five, is living with William Hatchett. By now she seems well over Savage, and to have her second child, a baby boy, with the twenty-seven-year-old bookman.

Into this happy period Pope unleashes *The Dunciad* – an epic about writers he's decided are dunces. He has a go at a range of people who in his view have sold out but Haywood, the only woman, is the star. The key scene is a race involving London's booksellers where the winner gets Eliza and all her rubbishy novels. She'll sell herself to the highest bidder, of course, because she's still so poor.

There's more; she's a breeder of fatherless brats: 'She had 2 Bastards, others say three'. Someone who cares should stop him. Further on, Eliza's the prize in a pissing contest. And Elizabeth Haywood writes crudely?

You can imagine her sigh as she reads this, her raised eyebrow as she finds breakfast for her five-year-old then sits down to breast-feed the baby while writing at the kitchen table. Or... need this be so miserable? Haywood's an optimist. Maybe playful Hatchett read Pope's doggerel aloud, impersonating pompous old Alexander, and they laughed til they cried, and the babies laughed too because something was so funny.

Which brings us to another thing Pope probably can't stand: Haywood is a cougar, lively and attractive enough to have a younger lover (I'm going to need to think about this later). I wish we knew a bit more about Hatchett, a translator and playwright and her partner, friend and supporter for two decades.

Let's wind up with the best part of Haywood's story. At fifty-one, during the time she's running a bookshop and publisher's with Hatchett in Covent Garden's Great Piazza, she starts a magazine. What vitamins is this woman taking?

The Female Spectator, a biteback to the male *Spectator*, was the first periodical written for women by a woman. Haywood used it for all sorts of stuff, not just to publicise her own books and the shop, but to encourage girls to get educated and see themselves as powerful in a world run by men. The magazine took the form of quirky essays alongside fictional letters from readers, which were responded to by four straight-talking women. The first of these is herself, the Female Spectator – a sexually experienced urban writer and unmarried mother. The other three voices, all invented, are probably the result of conversations she had with her pals. Which sounds quite like Candace Bushnell's *Sex and the City.*

The women offer seasoned insight on everything from gambling to love and lying. 'My life, for some years, was a con-tinued round of what I then called pleasure, my whole time engross'd by a hurry of promiscuous diversions. I never was a beauty, and am now very far from being young... But I have run through as many scenes of vanity and folly as the greatest coquet of them all.' Everyone makes mistakes, but some are entertaining, and all provide experience.

Eliza kept coming up with new ways to write for money. Hatchett died in his forties, and she wrote that final, ground-breaking book as a tribute. She died at sixty-three, apologizing in the last issue of *The Young Lady*, her new magazine for women, that she was too ill to write more at the moment.

Haywood was always balanced, but writing helped her stay

that way. In her thirties, she put Savage in the past and chose something less flashy and far more satisfying. She's lucky she got the chance, but maybe she engineered it. And while she and Hatchett were together, her work was fired by easy-going confidence and fun.

✳

If I was reading all this now and hadn't at least tried to do the things I've done, I'd be sobbing. These women did it over three hundred years ago. Well, hah, I held down some seriously freaky work and I definitely played with love. Obviously not with unalloyed great results. But I haven't had cystitis or an STD for – oh, a while.

'And what else? We've seen some writing that earned you income, but what is this you're writing now, with us in it?'

I'm back from the kitchen with my fifth mug of Aldi coffee to see two people at my desk, one of them actually in my chair. Aphra Behn is having fun with the mouse, moving the cursor around my screen and laughing a deep, entertained boom. Her skirt is rucked up, one calf crossed over her thigh, a pointed knee rakishly exposed. She's smoking a pipe, tobacco with a rich vanilla aroma. This is beyond annoying, since I gave up smoking with real difficulty.

At her side, Eliza Haywood is perusing the screen, leaning over Behn's shoulder and wearing my glasses. 'Greatest coquette of them all,' she murmurs. 'Thrilling but exhausting. Now, these spectacles. Look.' She turns her head to one side then the other, hands in the air. 'Struts that go over the ears, all holds itself in place.' I can't bear to tell her those struts became available about the year she died. 'And everything so clear.' If only.

'Cystitis!' Behn snorts. 'Tell me about it. And what is this "STD"?'

Cough briefly. 'Excuse me.' Put my mug on the desk, moving Aphra's elbow. 'That isn't actually edited.' I'm conscious

119

that, as well as being hacks, these women are published authors.

'Oh, editors are invaluable.' Haywood, kindly, over the top of my hornrims.

Behn kicks back in my jumper-draped chair. 'That's not quite right, about myself and Hoyle. I think now he was wholly homosexual, could never have loved me. Perhaps loved no one. Some men cannot give themselves.'

'And some women can't,' suggests Haywood, appraising my polo-neck.

'But why cause myself such pain,' Behn, drama queen, 'chasing the unattainable?'

'Distraction. Turbulence.' Eliza sips my coffee and quickly puts it down. 'I hear you looked wretched when you were finishing *The Rover*. Made it a marvellous play.'

'Perhaps.' Exactly. Too much heartache doesn't help at all. Behn shrugs. 'Terrible end he came to.' Though he outlived her, Hoyle was stabbed after a tavern brawl. 'Tsk.'

He wrote the epitaph on your grave, I mention. Who allowed that mistake? 'Here lies a proof that wit can never be/Defence enough against mortality.'

'Dum de dum de dum, sweet, like a nursery rhyme. And that's the bit of writing he's known for? Something about me?'

She taps the mouse again. Brightly: 'So what is an STD?'

She doesn't know? How stupidly lucky is that?

9

I was right about the poisoned chalice. I might look the part by now, with my hair extensions, carrion crow rings and arms so rammed with rubber bracelets and clattering crap I could barely move them, but inside I was still Bo-Peep. I wasn't ready for the demand to be backstage at key gigs, getting my picture taken and getting written about in the gossip columns (of my own magazine; who else would care?). And I wasn't ready for the down 'n' dirty in-fighting with the staff, who detested my goody two-shoes rise.

Backstage ligging? Actually, I wasn't going out much at all. I got home late from cover meetings. I woke in the dark, planning issues at the kitchen table before Paul appeared in pyjamas, hair on end, and said, 'What you doing, love?' I dropped my goth regalia, which you only have time for if you're not very busy, and borrowed Paul's polo shirts, which came in camo shades, like I expected to be dodging bullets in Phnom Penh. I pulled out the extensions and got my hair chopped off at a local barbers, short and ready for combat.

Walking into the office every day was a cross between *Watership Down* when the rabbits get myxomatosis and *Apocalypse Now.* That art editor, let's call him Cuthbert, was a tall, buck-toothed, hugely fat man with a shaved head and a high-pitched voice. 'You fucking BITCH!' he liked to squeak if I mentioned any qualm about a layout. 'You don't know a fucking THING. I'm going to get this scalpel and shred your face to a bleeding PULP.' The female sub would frown at me if we bumped into each other in the toilets. 'You really look like you're struggling. But you only got this job because Colin fancies you. Everyone knows that.'

I was barely seeing Paul. Before I got this job, I'd been frustrated: Paul didn't want to even try drugs, though I was desperate to find out what it was like. He was happy spending Sunday ironing shirts, making quiches (oh yes) and listening to Brubeck.

Now he suggested it might be best to leave – was this the time to get married? Shouldn't we be having kids? Maybe he thought I'd start wearing clothes more suitable for a building society manager's girlfriend.

One evening, just as I was crashing toward some sort of breakdown (well, I knew the way), one of the freelances – the intellectual goth with the dyed blue-black hair – called to ask if I was doing anything. I was the only person still in the office. Paul was at a regional managers' get-together. I said I could probably go with Nick to watch some 'radical dancers' at the Town & Country, then I hung up. He was asking me? My hands shook so badly I fumbled the receiver and it crashed to the desk.

So we saw these dancers, La La La Human Steps, with bare-chested Louise Lecavalier, who threw herself and her platinum dreadlocks around the stage like fireworks, and they were wild and dangerous. Then me and Nick went to the pub and I got drunk and he – he asked me intense questions. Well, maybe he didn't, maybe he asked me one and I poured my guts all over the floor. Because I'd read his features, and I saw he was wolfish and wry but fathomlessly intuitive, so when he asked me one thing I knew he'd asked me everything I wanted to be asked. The raw soul-deep excavations he put to Tom Verlaine or, surprisingly, an early riot grrrl band, the sort of thing Paul never asked. Nick had been out with the pretty one in the riot grrrl band, and before that Anja, the ghostly Teutonic vocalist from Xmal Deutschland. In his Oxfam dinner jacket, a cigarette between his fingers, he was a sexy vampire. There should have been a biohazard sign above his head.

*

'The narcissistic man...' Eliza replaces the mug with a cup of herbal tea. 'Loves only himself,' she reminds me. *The Female Spectator* knew all about those men.

Aphra is pacing the room. 'Just the hair-cutting alone,' she mutters. 'Like the mad scene in *Black Narcissus*.'

She notices a snap of Steve on some beach years ago and reaches for it. 'Ooh. Who's this?'

Eliza says, 'Put that down.'

'But is this...?'

'I said down. Good God.'

'It's not. Or she wouldn't have it here. So can I say, H.O.T.'

'Aphra.' Eliza folds her arms. 'It's the behaviour of a slut, you know? Haven't you learned anything?'

Pick up one of my little rubberized animals, useful for RSI. Repetitive Strain Injury: that's life in a nutshell, innit? Twist the innocent rubber hippo. Learned anything...

*

I saw him again that weekend, when Paul was helping his dad move a wardrobe. Yes, I saw Nick, because that wordy, writing magic had me by the throat. We went to the zoo and he fed the sea lions a fish, and me a bucketful of lines any woman should've seen coming, but not me, because I'd grown up virtually with the Amish then lived with Paul, who I'd made into the brilliant Dad I never had. I pointed out a funny child and Nick blinked his ice-blue eyes and grinned. 'Sorry? You're the only thing here I can focus on...' Perhaps he needed glasses too, more than anyone.

I left Paul, with whom sex, if we had it at all, was painful, sometimes impossible because I couldn't let go. I moved out of our pretty garden flat and into the rat-infested Shepherd's Bush swamp Nick shared with half a ton of vinyl and several billion free-range bacteria. And soon, with underwear he'd mind-blowingly torn off me (in five minutes, first with a grimy, moistened finger and then his hyper-experienced dick, my sexual problems vanished, although of course they were just beginning) and tender, funny love poems he scrawled in luminous felt pen on the wall (of a rented flat). For some reason, as soon as I'd done this cowish thing, the magazine's staff started to like me. Or maybe it was because I'd suddenly lost any ability to hold down the job. I got in late, in unwashed clothes. I couldn't concentrate. They were hugely entertained. Nick couldn't believe I stayed in the office so late, and once six o'clock had come and gone, would call every half an hour: 'Baby, why aren't you here in my arms?' Well, yes, why?

It's not as if his evening was short. He stayed up into the small hours, smoking dope, dancing to Lou Reed, so I did too (it's a bedsit, there's no option). Nick noted that Paul and I were tragically middle class, because we had a mortgage. I stared at him. This mortgage was a breakthrough. When obviously we should have been bohemian, like him. Only later did I discover Nick's dad was an advocate, or barrister, in Stirling, where he grew up in a big though damp house he'd inherit, so he could spend his twenties (and thirties and forties) being as bohemian as he liked. Proper jobs were for losers. In the middle of one of my worry sessions, which I was trying to hide at great cost, he shrugged and said, 'Resign.'

Leave the job I'd wanted all my life? What would we live on? Nick put a nicotine-stained hand gently over my mouth then began to remove my clothes. 'Come, lovely cat, my heart is amorous...' He was very good on Baudelaire. And fabulous sex, when you discover it at twenty-seven, is the gift that binds like shackles.

So I quit, because just maybe I could write freelance. I felt a flood of relief as I put down the phone, because I'd never have to cope with Cuthbert's PMT or any of the rest of those bastards again. And then it felt as if the floor had dissolved. Now what? Well, now Nick wasn't living with his boss any more, but with some unemployed tart. The next week he was scouted by *NME*, where he might be able to write more of the arcane, scorchingly poetic reviews that had been over the heads of many *Racket* readers, who were mostly from places like Doncaster and Swindon and felt he was patronizing them. But of course he'd never do that.

It's all too shit. What I need now is a pioneering woman writer with no romantic traumas. And I think I have one.

Walking through the brambles beside a wagon train is seventeen-year-old Abigail Scott. Second of nine surviving children, she was born in a log cabin in 1834 to farmers in the settler community of Groveland, Illinois. Newspapers have put 'Oregon fever' in her dad's head; the West is a land of plenty, his cash flow worries will be over. Though his wife's just had her twelfth child and doesn't want to go, he organises thirty people and five ox-drawn wagons and everyone begins the 2,400 mile long walk. Desperate to write, Abbie gets the job of keeping a journal so the group can trace what happens to them in this crazy land.

It seems they're walking through hell. Abbie's mother dies of cholera near Fort Laramie; sweet three-year-old Willie, since the baby's death the youngest in the family, gives up two months later beside the Burnt River. Improvised funerals, and the survivors trudge on.

And here's Abigail. 'When the mind is determined, it can do almost anything. I left home with a firm determination to be contented, and I have succeeded so well that I now cannot call myself anything but happy.' After losing your mother, brother, even your almost-sweetheart (John, drowned)? Partly because of that. Life can flicker out at any moment, so get the joy you can. She's in a new world, in a body becoming a woman's. Almost invincible.

Eight months later, a pitiful handful reach their destination: Lafayette, in the Willamette Valley. Barely populated, and so far without the petty restrictions of Illinois. Space for different ways to think, or that's the theory.

Abigail teaches, and at eighteen marries Ben Duniway, a darkly handsome horse rancher, better looking than her, a catch. They settle on Ben's land claim in Clackamas County, nicknamed 'Hardscrabble'; arid and rocky, poor drainage. Abigail's life is drudgery – washing, sewing, darning, cooking, cleaning, milking. Ben works so hard there are soon hired hands and Abbie cooks, washes, darns for them too. And she's pregnant, then again, and again.

One thing keeps her going: at night, sending letters and then features to local paper *The Oregon Farmer*, talking bluntly about her life. Things must change. Men were making new rules, but women were the packhorses who had to make them happen. Attacks continued by the Chinooks, Nez Percé or Western Shoshone, tribes being exterminated and launching terrifying retaliatory swoops. Alone in the candlelight, wind screaming, baby fretfully asleep, she described her isolation – the thing that drove pioneer women mad, so that they howled, hissed or sat silent, too horrified by their existence to speak. She is still just twenty-two.

The farm was wiped out overnight when a fire turned it into

126

smoking ash. They moved to a smaller farm with what was left. The first year's crops were washed away by floods. While her husband tried to salvage anything not rotted, Abigail found her journals of the family crossing and, based on that death-spattered trek and with multiple female heroines, her book *Captain Gray's Company* appeared two years later, one of the first novels to be published in Oregon. It was panned for creaky plot and bad grammar, but she'd done it.

And then, helping a friend, Ben pledged the farm as collateral for a loan. The friend defaulted, and the Duniways had to hand over their keys. They found a cramped cottage and Ben got a job wagon driving. In the dust and sweat he lost control of the horses. He was trampled and left disabled. Kind, pretty, doomed in all but his choice of wife.

What you gonna do, Abbie? Mid-twenties, with a crippled husband, four tiny children, Clara, Willis, Hubert, Wilkie, joined soon by Clyde and Ralph. You miss your baby brother. Your own babies must stay alive.

Abbie teaches again, drops that and opens a millinery store, listening and making mental notes as working-class women like her pour out their hearts. They're being punched, kicked and beaten by their men, who leave them and take the children, because women, who can't vote, like Abigail have no say.

Years go by. Benjamin finally lands a decent job at the US customs office and the family move to Portland. Where Abigail's younger brother Harvey is junior editor of *The Oregonian*. He's never liked her but she pays a social visit, asking silly questions. 'Quickly, Abigail. I'm busy.'

Just a month later, he hears this bitch of a sister has bought a small printing press and is launching a radical newssheet, *The New Northwest* – with her sons, in their teens, helping man the presses and Ben, who was proving extremely good at office work, managing its business matters at night.

The New Northwest is like an early *Guardian*, liberal and leftist. Abigail writes like there's no tomorrow, or won't be unless she hammers it out, campaigning for disenfranchised native Americans, the numerous local Chinese and the fight for women's votes. She accompanies women's rights campaigner Susan B Anthony along the Pacific Northwest coast. Local presses can't bear it. 'Women don't want to vote,' says a banner feature. 'A women's ballot would make great trouble in the family.' Wives would be corrupted and beautiful girls depraved by ugly harpies.

Abbie ran instalments of her novels in the paper, too: good stories with a motivating thrust. She wrote about her first dip in the sea, at forty. 'You take a strange delight in watching the surf as it creeps, murmuring, toward you, shaking its white locks in your face. You brace yourself, meet and conquer it, watch it receding for a fresh onslaught, while you stand your ground, victorious.'

And then in 1886 her daughter Clara, thirty-two, died of TB. Clara Bell had been Abbie's wingwoman, at meetings loudly singing the suffrage songs her mother wrote. Broken, Abigail sold *The New Northwest* to concentrate on the cause, which was something Clara utterly believed in.

And the tide was turning. Rural Oregon at last overwhelmingly supported women's rights. The people were poor but they were in it together, and men knew their mothers, sisters, aunts had been heroic on the plains. Why were businessmen and politicians keeping rights away from these women?

✳

'See?' Abigail, darning a pair of Steve's socks, bites the thread. 'Just when you've given up on men, they surprise you.' She sniffs. 'Some of 'em.'

✳

And in 1912, Oregon at last relented and women got a say in how their county was run. Duniway, who'd seen effigies of herself burned, was a white-haired seventy-eight, but the first woman to vote. 'The young women of today,' she wrote, 'free to study, speak, write, to choose their occupation should remember that every inch of this freedom was bought for them at a great price. It is for them to help the reforms of their own times, by spreading the light of freedom and of truth.'

In 1915, she travelled to San Francisco to demand all American states let women vote, which they didn't do until 1920. She died a few months later of infection from a gangrenous toe which, typically, she'd tried to treat herself.

✳

And what did I do, to spread the light of freedom and of truth? In my new, mildewed home, to which I had brought the two unsuspecting cats I had at the time, I looked for work, and launched myself, in Nick's wake, at *NME*, where they received me graciously, an ex-big fish flumping like a turbot onto their sleek ocean-going deck.

We don't hear a lot more about Ben Duniway; but despite his mistakes, it seems he really was Abbie's lifelong friend. He played a quiet, supporting role, enabling his wife to vault into her own kind of stardom, letting her be as strong as he always knew she was. So she chose wisely too, in the end.

And the choice I'd made? Well, I spent most of the next six months drunk, or on drugs. I discovered I was not just compulsive but a boozer like my sculptor granddad, working my way through spliff and acid, cider, vodka, cheap wine.

Mixed with shagging. Me and the dark-hearted goth had sex on empty late-night tube trains, rattling high on the Metropolitan line; inside galleons in ghostly, snow-covered kids' playgrounds and once, amusingly, in a hammock. I also ligged like I'd never ligged before, following Nick, embarrassed by every second – didn't every ligger feel superfluous when the band had finished and clearly wanted to say please push off? That never occurred to Nicholas. The bands were his friends, they'd be devastated if he wasn't there. Even the Pixies, so popular you had to fight like a maniac to get backstage? Shy Elizabeth Fraser of the Cocteau Twins? (Ah, but he understood her.) Even Blondie, on their second comeback? Yes, Debbie Harry looked for him specifically.

In addition to being a Beat poet, Nick was a feminist, he said so. I didn't smoke and, to help me be cool and partake as an equal in the rock lifestyle, he bought me my own cigarettes, Gauloises Blondes, from an outlet in Old Compton Street. Asthmatic, I struggled at the start but with Nick's support I became proficient. Much easier to stay up socialising then write all night with a cigarette. I reviewed The Cramps at the Dominion, and thought how like the camp and confident Lux Interior and Poison Ivy we were. More accurate would be the night we saw Sonic Youth, and Iggy Pop appeared at the encore. 'Now I wanna be your dog/ And I'll lay right down in my favourite place.' In a clattering blaze, I wrote it up as a Beat poem at our cat food-stained plastic table. *A Beat poem?*

With Nick as my Svengali, by now I looked like Courtney Love crossed with Prince's Apollonia. Approximately. Corset. Vinyl mini. Stockings with suspenders, visible due to the short skirt. Scuzzy kitten heels. I was in a transport of lust and physical pain. (The shoes, the corset, the *cold*.) I met Paul one afternoon to sort out finance; guilt-ridden, I was walking away with next to nothing. We met in McDonald's by Tottenham Court Road tube, and he didn't recognize me. I'd hurt him badly, but he could probably see the girl he'd known was gone.

Feeling very low, I caught sight of myself in a window as I left the cafe. Who is that tottering tramp? I pushed through the crowds. And the thing is, I hadn't just lost who I was. I'd forgotten how I used to write.

✳

We didn't have enough money. Nick couldn't do much but review, but I got a load of production shifts on things like

She, Best, Prima and ironically the *Clothes Show Magazine*. It felt great to be out of the flat. I'd get up, feed the cats and take Nick his breakfast in bed. He liked Weetabix with Smarties. Maybe that's why his teeth were so bad. Well, that or the speed.

And then two things happened. In fact, three.

First, I got pregnant. You were ahead of me here, probably. I'd been slipshod in my use of the cap; in fact, I may have been so out of it I assumed it was still in from last time and just used an extra pessary. I knew being pregnant was a mistake, but the morning I tested, I went to the common on my own (Nick wasn't awake) and let myself feel briefly overjoyed. Which surprised me, because I'd never wanted children. I thought Nick would find this as iconoclastic as I did – a baby! – and we could at least talk about it. Because apparently as well as a sex goddess I was rivers of stardust and moonlight, so what might our little child be? Would he say we should go ahead? Beg me, try to convince me? He didn't. Even though he'd never known love like this before, when I told him, he went back to sleep. When he got up, he asked peevishly – he was due to play tennis. *Tennis?* – if I'd called the doctor yet about an abortion.

Next, with that scheduled and my heart in my boots, I got what I thought was another bout of cystitis. Except going to the loo felt like I was trying to release a stream of razor blades. Exhausted one night by having a piss, I slumped, close to tears, back to the dirty bedroom. Nick was halfway through his own creative Camberwell Carrot, and when I told him why I'd interrupted his TV viewing with whimpers, he looked briefly awkward. 'Got something wrong, haven't I?'

I blew my nose, trying to find a way to sit in bed without it seeming I was straddling a particularly sharp hatchet. 'Something..?'

'Herpes.' Was this new, he'd just got this? But how? 'Had it years, told you.'

I'd understood that he'd caught something but been treated and got rid of it. Anyway, now I had it too, even though for the bloke, it's often not difficult to spot the large red sore on your dick, so it's your option to have sex when you're contagious or alert the person you're about to give this to, as a present, and ask if they'd prefer something else.

Since Nick had passed me this baton when I was pregnant and pulsing with blood and hormones, the first attack was particularly grim – blisters not just genitally but on my fingers too. I felt like Freddie from *Nightmare on Elm Street*. I had to postpone the abortion. The worst was that the herpes medication was apparently damaging the embryo. The morning sickness increased. I played the Penguin Café Orchestra's *Perpetuum Mobile* over and over and the clear, clean notes briefly stopped the nausea. The baby kicked, danced in its watery bubble. It was as if a fairy had opened a trapdoor in my heart. I noticed it and carefully pushed it closed.

One afternoon Maggie came, sombre and loaded down with sorbets. She cleaned the stinking kitchen, and held cool flannels to my feverish forehead.

Now I had herpes, I'd never again be a blood donor. Nick had altered me, less Edward Cullen than Dracula; I'd become part of his undead tribe. In the street, if I was well enough to get to the shop, I saw normal people, but they didn't see me. And yet I still felt I could make something of this little sow's ear. Life can't be perfect.

I let myself out on the day of the abortion and walked to the hospital in the dark. Got through it. Woke so relieved not to be engulfed by waves of sickness that at least there seemed one good thing in this. Nick was an hour late to collect me because Chelsea were playing. When I told him I wasn't up to walking home, he said he didn't have change for a bus.

And finally he went on tour with the riot grrrl band that included his ex, and the first I heard of it was a phone call from

Heathrow Terminal 4. I'd been soaking filth off the kitchen floor, up to my armpits in a bucket of detergent, and I absently mopped suds from my arm with one of his T-shirts as I listened to his voice – 'I was in the meeting and I had to leave straight from there' – Patsy Cline, my cleaning music, crooning in the background.

No, I don't think so.

I packed up my own wagon train, with my cats, books, typewriter and postcard of the Chrysler Building. I sprayed, 'So long, fuckface' on the wall (I wish I had) and by the time he got back, I'd struck out for a brave new land.

✳

'You should've cut that thing off.'

It's Duniway, standing behind me, fists on her hips. Turn round and blink. 'You're right, Abigail. I absolutely should.'

Eliza Haywood hugs me, then gives me a girl power fist-bump.

Sitting cross-legged on the floor, Behn is amusing the cat with a piece of string. She nods. 'And burned it.'

✳

Nick had more spirochetes than the Earl of Rochester. Luckily, I had more antivirals. Still, that was the year I realised some passions are just wrong, and I reinforced my view as time passed with the help of additional amour fous. Foux? Eventually, my heart became a small compacted lump like a piece of debris salvaged from the moon.

But one passion felt pure, and fuelled me. Because not only did I emerge remade from the crucible of Nick's dump, but so did the way I put down words. That got firmer but also more elastic, a reaction to the style he used but boosted by cynicism and a sense of liberation. Transmuted, I myself was tempered steel, shiny, like a blade. I knew there might eventually be some lighter-hearted, airy phoenix rising, but that couldn't happen yet. For now, I just hosed the sticky fluff and

133

Beat poetry from my head and soul and anything I wrote. The Beats treated their women like shit.

✳

A private flame I clung to was that one day I'd write something genuinely worthwhile. Because it's been lovely meeting the people I've interviewed but sometimes I think, even features are glorified press releases. It's worse with the marketing I currently churn out.

'You had a use for that.' A western seaboard voice. 'It paid the bills. But maybe now you need a new direction. For me there was always a different challenge, and that gave me energy. So I didn't tire, a phrase you use a lot.'

That's what Abigail would say. Having crossed deserts, had six children and opened a paper that helped lead a revolution, on the back of a year's education.

I should perhaps consider what my new challenge might be, because there is a dream, clearly: writing a book. Behn, Haywood, Duniway all created something that came from their hearts. What stops me trying? Oh, failure. Finding the time when I should be looking for work. Staring into myself and seeing the void of no imagination...

'You've got the imagination to come up with us here, talking to you.' Eliza Haywood's calm tone. Of course, I'll never know how she really sounded.

'Unless you're having another breakdown. That's possible.' Aphra Behn, shrugging on her jacket.

'Well no, it isn't actually. At the moment.' Though I'm talking back to them. Under my breath. Quite enjoying it.

'Liza's right.' Duniway stands. They're going. 'None of it's happening. All made up. You're sitting here on your own, honey.'

Thanks. And when I look around, I am.

So. Book. About..? Well, what you've been writing for nine chapters, darling. The quest for how to make it work out when you're common. And not be anxious or scared. Interestingly, a way for me to do both these things in the past has been trying to write something decent and not giving up on it when life gets tricky. Like a cat, writing's a familiar you can summon, and sometimes it scratches but mostly it's pleased to see you. Here we both are.

'God's balls, get on with it!' Aphra, back to pick up a dropped earring.

'I'm going to.'

'Good. By the way, Sally Salisbury, downstairs. Crazy.'

'Slightly sweeping but yep. It's what's happened to her.'

'I like her for it.'

'Me too.'

Huff on my lenses, wipe them with a tissue. I'm going to find room for this. Whether or not I owe it to myself, and I do, I owe it to my lay-deez.

10

Rebel, rebel

Find a safe house or even, yes, a room.
And get what you need, but learn to give

Friday night at the Dog & Bone in Deptford. And my favourite person, William Wallace, who is not in fact Scottish but Irish (the lyrical, voluble sort), is in, roaring drunk, seventy-four and beautiful in his suit and tie. He's spotted two newbies, a young couple who've drifted through the door by mistake and are wondering whether they should stay or they should go because if you're new you *would* think, Ooh, it could turn nasty in here. And once or twice it has but everyone knows how to cope with that. The pair stand undecided while Jim Morrison casually asks, 'Don't you love her madly? Wanna be her daddy...'

Steve doesn't love me madly. His jaw is set. He looks at his mobile, puts it away, looks again. I've been offhand this week, taking out my unhappiness with myself on him, but this evening since he got in I have made a stab at conversation, tried to open up a mollifying dialogue, quite important when you know alcohol will be involved. Apparently, though – even after him coming home late every night, at five-a-side football or stuck at work, so that this should be a welcome chance for both sides to resume amicable communication – it's another monosyllabic day. I can always tell when something's about to kick off.

''Nother one?' He's looking at the table. I say okay and watch him go. Study his profile at the bar. The angular face shape, the stubble. Deep-set eyes I think are hazel but he insists are green because he's London Irish and everything must be. He's beautiful, far more so than Bill Wallace. I know it but I don't see it, or I see it and ignore it. Is he mine, if I want him? Can't be, or if so he must have a fault. In general I go for the wrong men, narcissists like dad. Loathsome, so attractive, energy, ego. Steve has almost no narcissism, but if on occasion he exhibits it I don't like it. He can't win. Don't you want to shake me?

A woman staggers over to sit beside me. How much have Steve and I had to drink? How much has she had?

'Not seen you in here before.'

Well, we've been here, I say. She takes my hand and strokes it. Look down at where our fingers clasp. My hand's battered from clothes washing, but hers is a claw, craggy with years of cleaning or tough living and with several big gold rings. 'Where djoo live? Round 'ere?' We chat, I feel slightly awkward but surely I'm just making a pal? She says, 'Come and dance.' Steve's being such a dick I might as well.

She grabs me round the waist, spinning me, we're jiving, she's quite good actually. Dusk sunlight glimmers through the dirty windows, lighting up bits of floating dust and dog hairs, it's such a great spring evening. Glimpse Steve's face, rigid though predictably he's looking away. Just as I decide to sit down she confirms my hunch, saying in my ear, 'You straight or gay?'

'Er, I'm with him.' I gesture.

Her lips pull back in derision. 'Who's *he*?'

Reach our table and Steve says, 'Finish your drink. We're leaving.

Oh, really? As he heads to the gents, fumble for my glasses, pick up his mobile and look at his messages. Or try to. I see the name 'Samina', his boss at this grim bid-writing company, before he's back, snatching it out of my hand – 'What d'you think you're doing?' – and taking it with him.

We walk home in silence. Once the front door is closed, I say, 'So why you texting Samina on a Friday night?'

'Because she's a decent woman.'

He begins to feed our veteran cat Flossie, who has a thyroid condition and is desperate for food and whining annoyingly.

'Well, I expect she's got her own life, then.'

'I'm sure she has.'

'Yet you interrupt it at the weekend?'

'Yes, because I felt like being in touch with someone who might care about me and what I had to say even slightly.'

Struggle drunkenly with getting my bloody arm out of my bloody sleeve and throw the jacket on the sofa, where it falls off into another cat-food bowl. 'I ask you to speak to me, nothing. Or one-word responses. *Anal*. Because of your stupid family and your repressed Catholic mother.'

'I see. And who's your dykey friend, out of interest?'

'Dunno.' Shoulder past him with the two empty cat bowls and start washing them.

'You'll flirt with anyone, won't you? Apart from me. Because all the time, you're thinking about someone else. I've tried to work out what it is and that must be it, one of your crappy exes that you're still hung up on even though they treated you like shit.'

I *am* thinking about someone else a lot of the time, and he must know who. But it's too late for that, because here it comes. 'Well, you treat *me* like shit. You bitch.'

Oh dear. Hello Irish temper tantrum. I always like to trot out the Irish thing and my resentment of it because I'd thought when I met his family that I would be welcomed into the homestead – a 1970s terrace on a Haringey council estate adapted for Steve's mother's MS – with penny whistles and open arms. But his mother ignored me, ricocheting her wheelchair round me with a speed that suggested I wasn't there. His dad and one of his brothers had the snooker on. When I walked in, that brother Liam got up, turned the sound as high as it would go and sat back down. They're a family who barely speak, though I'm sure they can, and their dislike of me has never faded. According to Steve it's because I'm English. But we're in England, it's odds-on I'm going to be.

I'm getting off the point. Though I do sigh and say, 'Is this connected to how your mum neglected you?'

'I don't know what I'm doing in this relationship. Frankly, it doesn't exist. Any other woman would behave better than you. Kinder. Halfway loving.'

'But –'

'*Listen* to me!'

His fists are clenched. I'd be surprised if there was physical violence but it's what I grew up with, so I'm braced. I see now though why Mum goaded Dad at times. You just – your blood gets up, you're frightened but furious too.

I try, calmly, saying, 'Can we...'

'Get out of my face! Just fuck *RIGHT OFF!*'

But it's him who slams the door, storming into the traffic-laden night.

✳

He's done this before. Sometimes when he slams out I go to look for him, stomping in pyjamas and my coat down Trafalgar Road, with its Polish offies, vape shops and litter-strewn newsagents selling five-pound wraps and Twixes at one in the morning. I try his mobile; always off. Once I called Maggie, who an hour or so later called back and said ring your A&E. Which I did. Not long after that I heard his key. He went to bed and I slept on the sofa because you need space and safety.

✳

On Saturday he hugs me. 'I'm a fekkin' eejit. What am I?'

Phew. Turn away, eyes screwed up with relief. And guilt, because whose fault is this really? 'Fekkin' eejit.'

'And I love you.'

'Yeah, right.'

✳

Monday evening. Halfway through eating his pasta, his mobile goes. He checks it and smirks. 'Samina's boyfriend's as bad as you in terms of neurotic behaviour.'

'She's confiding in you?'

'Oh,' breezily, 'we talked about her man today. She takes no shit. He – Nathaniel, get him – seems all right, puts in the hours, like she does. But she could do better.'

He talks about all this with Samina? I go and sit in the bedroom, open a book and stare at the floor.

If anything was going on, Steve wouldn't offer tonight's information. Or would he, since he knows I looked at his phone once already? Turn a page. Is there anything here I should be paying attention to?

Samina is really pretty. I mean gorgeous. Genuine, warm, the one time I met her. Much younger than me. Steve would look great with her. They'd be planning a family.

✳

I'm impressed by the positivity I felt when I split up with Nick. I had no home, no money, virtually no work but I was full of the hope and energy that comes with liberty. At first I stayed with Maggie, who had a box-room in a Turnpike Lane flat. I got more shifts on *She* and by night scoured London for somewhere to rent. I saw a scary hole above the shops on Streatham High Road and a room in Norbury in the home of a big Indian family who asked if I could give my cats to a refuge.

And then I realised a mortgage would be cheaper than renting. In London in the late 80s this was really true, it's just that people I knew, most of them rock writers, didn't talk about buying. Now I know some of them had lovely backgrounds, were taking time out to be alternative and would eventually be given a property or the money for one by their parents, but at

140

the time I felt so visionary in providing for myself, I could hardly stand it. I had £4,700 for a deposit, money Paul gave me when I left him with the flat we'd spent years jointly paying for, which he'd later sell for £380,000.

I started my trawl out east, where property then was cheaper. A dungeon in Plaistow. A studio in Newham where I could run a ladder from the bedroom so the cats could get out onto a bathroom roof. And then, lost, I was in Hackney. No one wanted to go to Hackney in 1989, it was a bleak horrortown. Dalston market selling unidentified meat. Two greasy spoons with porno calendars on the walls in Stoke Newington. But Stokey is where I found myself, in every way. Run-down, boarded-up but with a curvy road and a basic park full of needles. I saw a flat on a Peabody estate with a door of its own that I could put a cat flap in. It cost £44,000 and I was on £50 a day. No one else wanted it.

The maisonette was tiny, but I'm not big. I slept on coats in the front room with a dressing-gown for a curtain and had a kettle, a lamp, a desk, my Olympia typewriter and a record deck. Everything else I'd had was Paul's. The cats prowled around, inspecting the steep staircase where, as in a lighthouse, the three rooms (the bathroom was a sectioned-off part of the kitchen, both so small I could touch every wall while standing in one spot) went off at angles. I painted Rilke poems all over the woodchipped bathroom walls, something that would have driven Paul mad. The half-fridge was a knock-off from a Dalston parts yard, I never had a washing machine, and the 1950s cooker was great shelving for books.

✳

I just had to pay that mortgage. I got shifts on left-wing listings mag *City Limits*. I got graveyard stints on the *Daily Telegraph*, arriving for work at 11pm, taking my lunch break in Fleet Street at two in the morning.

And then I started getting booked on the weekend magazine of a fairly salacious tabloid. My boss, production manager Sandy, sometimes wrote the horoscopes. If Sandy liked you she was fun, but if you were slow or made personal calls, her head with its blonde chignon would grind slowly, like Voldemort's, in your direction. If you irritated too much, you'd get the Stars to edit, and under your own sign read something like: 'Finding it hard to concentrate? Others have noticed. Avoid sheer drops this week. Could number 8 be lucky?'

I became institutionalised at the magazine. Sandy was a perfectionist; stories of her tethering subs to their desks until midnight on Christmas Eve were legendary. Checking facts on jacked-up celebrities and two-headed hamsters and writing for the rock press at weekends, I was too tired to think, jolting home on the 73 bus half asleep. I was on a treadmill, but at home now I had a wooden double bed and secondhand velvet curtains. Cosy, uninterrupted sleep rejuvenated me.

I got my first tattoo, a pink rose on a black stem. And then I did another very stupid thing. Reviewing a gig (Edie Brickell: 'What I am is what I am/Are you what you are or... what?') I bumped into Nick. We had a fling, of the kind you can only have with an ex you once worshipped, who says, 'I can't get you out of my mind...' It was all on my terms. Until I developed a deep pain in my lower abdomen. I *know*, but I'd asked and he assured me, hurt, that he was fine, no diseases, nothing. That he knew about. He just had something he didn't know about, chlamydia, from fucking an air hostess on the way back from interviewing Guns N' Roses. I'd had it for months by the time I realised. Until, left undiagnosed ('It's cystitis again,' said my doctor. 'Make sure you empty your bladder') it turned into Pelvic Inflammatory Disease, which is where all the meaningful parts of you feel like they're being napalmed. You ask how I could have been so moronic; don't you think I ask myself the same thing? No excuse that in 1990, chlamydia and its lack of obvious symptoms was fairly new. Nick was ahead of his time when it came to STDs, an intrepid early adopter.

Anyway. That's how I got to know Genito-Urinary clinics so well. The big room in a shed at the Homerton off Mare Street. The ticket with a number. The hours of waiting, while pimps hung about outside, waiting for their girls to get clean.

Turned out I'd sustained quite serious internal damage. When I was finally rid of most of the issues Nick left me with, the doctor talked about extra protection for future relationships. I said there wouldn't be more relationships. Me and men didn't mix and life without them was perfect.

That Christmas, home alone after another argument with Dad, I bought myself a cheap mountain bike in Dalston. From the first test ride I was off my head. Despite kitten heels and the feather earrings which ripped back in the breeze and nearly tore my lobes off, despite the woman on a mobility scooter – 'Woah. Sorry! Hi-ho, Silver!' – I was in love L.O.V.E. you best believe it. We sped together down ugly streets and pretty ones, streets I was familiar with and streets I'd never seen. In an hour the bike could show me more of my world than I knew. This was my Pegasus, my perfect partner. It didn't make me ill, and it was far from boring.

I mapped out a route to work. No one else cycled to work, it was freak behaviour. 'How long d'you think it'll take?' I asked my neighbour, Pinball Geoff. He shrugged, loading vintage pinball machine Viva! Las Vegas, his latest sale, into his van. 'Stokey to King's Cross by bike? Two hours?' It was forty minutes. I chucked the jewellery and wore leggings, a vest top and my biker jacket, hair in a peaked cap. Doc Martens, good for kicking bumpers. Wraparound shades, because you can get grit in your eyes on a bike and more than once I've had to go to Moorfields. I looked like a camp dispatch rider.

Forget being a girl. I just needed to be myself and make my own world. As I cut through standing traffic, as I rebuilt my health and got stronger from carrying the bike up flights of stairs, and as I also Polyfilla'd the gap round the bathroom window frame and sealed a ceiling crack while I sang along with Lou Reed ('Jackie is just speeding away, thought she was James Dean for a day...'), and got into a Stokey band (La Cura Para Del Amor) and started to actually look my boss in the face, I felt that world coming together.

Mary Frith aka Moll Cutpurse couldn't stand men, or not romantically. But then, she probably wanted to be one. 'Y'know?' She's leaning on the door frame, thumb in her belt, sardonic grin on her face; Cockney accent, a man's strides and a smoke on the go. (Lisa Dillon played her at the RSC with a short back and sides, swaggering and clutching her cock.) She was born maybe 1584 near the Barbican, where her father Ron Stuart made shoes. The family bordered on starvation, so Mary, Moll, occasionally Mal, was left to run amok. According to one year's copy of the *Newgate Calendar*, a sort of annual review of the local news with a moralistic slant, even as a child, 'She was above all breeding and instruction. She was a hoyden, and delighted only in boys' play or pastime. Many a bang and blow this hoyting procured her, but she was not so to be tamed...' Quite.

Since there's so often no food in the house, pretty soon, having failed at being a cleaner and a fortuneteller, she's stealing it. Her furious uncle sticks her on a ship to New England – they'll take anyone in the Colonies – but she's overboard and back like a greased rat. No one wants her, what's she going to do? Steal on a grander scale. In loose trousers and a man's doublet, a long clay pipe in her hand, she blends with the crowds, cutting the ties that hang women's purses from their belts, which is how she gets her name. She wasn't seen? 'Very busy. Cut quick wiv a knife, slip it all in your trews.'

Anyone can be in trouble all the time for theft. What makes Mary start to be mythical is this issue of dressing like a man, smoking (it's well known women can't stand tobacco) and swearing when she feels like swearing. Dressing like a man is 'indecent' and 'obscene'. It's unconventional, which for women is not allowed, but added to that menswear is less restrictive, and in virtually every era, including now in some ways, women's clothes are organised to make and keep them docile. In this respect Molly's not hurting anyone, but we know that doesn't matter if you're challenging the rules. 'Roaring boys' was the term for young working-class blokes who swaggered about yelling and being a bit dangerous. There's only one roaring girl, and before you know it a play, *The Roaring Girl*, by Thomas Middleton and Thomas Dekker, has been written about her. It's incredibly fair, actually. Its star is a clever, unusual woman who, though she's seen as shocking, is in fact a sensible free-thinker.

Moll even performs in the play once (still illegal at this time), bantering with the audience – 'You over there. Thass it, you mate. Wadja fink I am, man or a woman? Or a bit of both? Wanna see me credentials? Yaah, look at him, he's terrified.'

Still stealing, she's branded on the hand four times and sentenced to public penance, standing in a white sheet near

St Paul's during the Sunday sermon. I'm surprised she didn't try and do a puppet show.

And by her thirties, she's working as a pimp. No? Yes, but unconventionally. She finds women for men, but she also finds respectable male lovers for married middle-class wives. She's discreet and conscientious – when one wife makes a deathbed confession about lovers Molly's found her, she says Moll convinced the men to send money toward the upkeep of children that were probably theirs.

Moll insists she herself has no interest in sex. Which I don't buy. What with running a high-end dating agency and occasionally performing to sing filthy songs, she's finally making money. Where does she live? In a house in Fleet Street, just opposite Shoe Lane, kept clean by three maids. She's got parrots, she's got mastiffs (each with its own bed with blankets) and there are mirrors on every wall, so even though one newssheet calls her 'an Ugly', she can't be. Attractive and knows it. And you think, aha. Three young maids?

She possibly married in 1614, at thirty, for convenience and so that at future trials she wouldn't be a 'spinster' with no rights – she and her husband shook hands once the deal was done and said a cheerful farewell.

In her fifties, it's rumoured she became a highwaywoman with her own gang. At the same time, she took in stolen goods and brokered their return to their owners for lots of money.

She definitely acted in another play, *Amends for Ladies*, which was again supposed to show her in a terrible light. While other women (played by men) discussed their happy lives as Stepford wives, Molly was there to show that by being free and independent she'd lost everything a woman should hope to be, and so wasn't anything at all. And yet again it made her look like the voice of reason.

And at sixty, because she wouldn't stop wearing men's clothes and being different and saying how good it felt, she was sent to Bethlem Royal Hospital for the insane, known as Bedlam. She emerged 'cured of insanity'. Lobotomy's probably the word we're looking for. A primitive kind. Skull opened up with chisels.

And maybe that achieved what it was supposed to, because when she recovered she was different: quiet, then depressed. According to the *Newgate Calendar*, she came out of hellish Bedlam 'grown crazy in her body, and discontented in mind'. She got dropsy, fluid retention in her joints, often caused by malnutrition – painful and finally crippling. She 'thought the devil had got within her doublet' (still feebly trying to wear men's clothes, then). She worried about everything. I just can't bear it. She died at seventy-four, at home in Fleet Street. Our daring joker, our handsome, headstrong Frances Farmer left her house to her maids, who looked after her to the end. And she asked to be buried face down 'because I am unworthy to look upwards, and as I have in my life been preposterous, so I may be in my death...'

✳

I want to smash something. Or roar.

'Well, don't do it on my account.' She tamps out her pipe, stuffs it in her pocket. 'At least I died in my own bed, unlike most famous villains. I wasn't happy but I'd *been* happy, and that's what matters.'

But not fair.

'Forget fair. Just get on with what you wanna do. You'll sustain lasting damage if you don't go after what feels right, however stupid some shitheads think it is.'

I do do what feels right. Well, I'm trying to.

'In the past, did what you were doing feel right?'

Mostly, if you mean work. Or with Nick? At the start I thought it did.

'You wanted it to be right but you were so naïve.' She laughs like a man. 'You know what you want a bit better now.'

147

Maybe. But in my personal life... I don't think I can get emotionally close anymore, it's not in me now.

'I've seen your search history. *Ten ways to tell if your cat loves you.*'

Something's died inside, that's the point.

'Oh, boo hoo. Well, try. Don't seize up from your heart to your honey pot.'

I beg your pardon?

'And hammer at the other venture, make it work or go down trying.'

I'm used up.

'You're not. And to be controversial, I wonder whether, if you hadn't gone off the rails with Nick, you'd regret it.'

I have no response.

'Maybe you needed it. Massive kick-start. As you've got older, I notice you tend to say no to things you need.'

Who's writing your script?

✳

There weren't many female footpads, a name I like for highwaymen. Though they were despised as unnatural, romance persisted about those who did exist – women who'd thrown off the shackles of domestic life and gone on a 'loose ramble', dressed as men and with pistols down their boots. Not easy. Tales of highwaywomen being abused by jailors... but just as many of jailors' wives not realising these raffish scoundrels were girls, losing their hearts and slipping them the key to their cell. People assumed no normal girl could bear the job's loneliness, women needed husbands, children. Yet again and again you see highwaywomen relishing sexual leeway, having the cash to vanish when a man was a letdown.

'Oh, it's all crap, yeah. I had my gang of female nickers with me, so you hardly lacked company.' Here come the girls, like Robin Hood's men but prettier. 'And there was always my galloping steed, my true companion. Buster.'

Buster?

'Above all I had my home – my hideaway and retreat. How could they prove I'd done those deeds, with such a neat and well-appointed residence?'

✳

There was no neatness to my Stokey sanctuary. Ashtrays and newspapers everywhere, and when Maggie came, 'The only stuff in your fridge is cheese and alcohol.' But like Molly, I had my gang. Toni, the wired Brooklyn rock hack squatting in Clapton, off her head alternately on lithium or speed. I met her first on *City Limits*, where between writing reviews she sat in on reception, and she'd call me from there for relationship updates, bellowing while the switchboard lit up, 'Leave him! Just leave him!' Charlie, the gangly Marie Helvin lookalike with the chipped tooth and biker boots, a magazine designer who'd struggled out of a Penzance terrace where her dad knocked her about and found a new life, like we all did, in London, cycling with me down the middle of Old Compton Street.

Me and Charlie met regularly on Saturdays for coffee breaks at Tuttons on Covent Garden's piazza, sprawled in the terrace's hot sun hooting about men we'd met, glances bouncing our way as Charles (real name not Charlotte but Sharon, reinvention is key) tossed her black curls and flaunted her tanned biceps. One Sunday night I left my bike, Trigger, at her Brixton council flat and got the bus home, too drunk to drive. She met me the following Saturday at Tuttons, riding like a highwaywoman out of the dazzling light, having led my steed alongside her own bike by its handlebars. She shrugged off the achievement. 'You need your horse, sweetheart.'

We did things like that for each other every week.

✳

Email. 'Stupid old bugger here.' Stefano! 'Look, I've heard you bashing away in there every morning. Are you finally trying

149

to write your thing, whatever it is? How about this; one of us is employed. Give yourself a month without looking for work and see what you come up with. And don't *worry*.'

We can't afford a scheme like that.

But I feel Moll's bravado fizz up in me. And what do we really need? Not much. Whereas I've seen Issy Fernandez at work when a booking falls through. In fact, once when that happened, she wanted a lunchtime walk with me so that I, a fellow freelance, could lament with her. As we strolled toward Russell Square I said, 'You'll be okay. It's a knockback but it's just one thing, you've got others and there's more out there.'

She inhaled. 'Don't you understand? The kids' school fees are enormous. Agamemnon's pony costs a bomb. We have a standing order at Berry Brothers, which I suppose I could put on pause. And they were about to start the new walk-in wardrobe...' Even though Anton is a marketing honcho on six figures and her mum must have a bit of spare change, I saw her dilemma.

And it looked like a prison, a prison I'm not in. So I'm going to buy myself time off from the tension of looking for work and salvage free moments by economising further. I glue a shoe where the sole's coming away. Buy cheap vats of nourishing henna conditioner and huge bottles of hemp seed oil and castor oil at knockdown prices from Caribbean Hair and Beauty in Deptford, the only white girl in there, and every time I visit either a woman is having a wig fitted, singing her head off, or tiny kids are giggling as they race each other up and down the aisles, hitting each other with long red and blonde wefts for weave-ons. I use hemp seed oil as a gentle moisturiser; it's purer than Clarins or Aveda, why did I waste my money there? I massage the castor oil into my scalp and through my hair, slowly instead of rushing, and the massage doesn't just help my hair stop falling out, it relaxes my tight neck muscles. Finally, I still rescue clothes from skips, which demonstrates a bit of Moll's native cheek while not actually being theft. Unlike the things in my wardrobe, many bought for work, these are clothes for the emerging me, a chancer and improvisor. Each step's like unlocking a manacle.

✳

It all works, for a few weeks. For that time it's wonderful. But I can't concentrate because I can't shift the shame. Steve gets in later and later, and I've been sitting on my arse. I can't justify it. And then there's an email from the bloke who used to feed our felines when we went away. 'Just lost my assistant. Know anyone who could help?' Of course I do.

✳

'So these are the cats for today. Nelson, who actually has got a damaged forepaw. Houdini, who will be hiding in the house or garden somewhere. You can't leave until you've found him and taken a picture, which you send to me and I'll forward it to the owner. And Oscar, who's overweight, so he's on a special diet. Scales on the worktop to measure his food. Do *not* overfeed him, they'll know.' Terry hands me the three sets of keys. This is my test week. And I'm determined. Pedal to Nelson's, a glitzy new tower block on the river that has a permanent wind tunnel around it. It's still being finished. As I negotiate the keypad on the outer doors, clutching my plastic carrier of scourer, rubber gloves, scoop and poo bags, notice I'm invisible to the people who live here. But the lowly mechanicals – the guy still wiring bits of the lift, the various cleaners, gardener, postman – all nod; we're the backup team, the chorus line, here to service the residents, the stars of the show, though we'll never see them. On the fourteenth floor, which looks just like the twelfth because I got off there by mistake, walk down the creepy corridor and let myself in. The flat stinks already, the vomity, dentist's/car showroom reek of the rubberised bathroom mixing with the tang of decaying food left on encrusted dishes on the worktop, presumably awaiting the cleaner, and the heady perfume of the litter tray. The floor-to-ceiling windows, giving a superb view far below of forklift trucks, cranes and a building site stretching at least as far as Charlton, are filthy, stained somehow both inside and out, and half-covered by long gauze curtains, and even those are dirty, as if they open them with pizza on their fingers. Someone will clean the curtains.

Under the bed, brow furrowed, is Nelson. 'Nelson... Don't be scared.' Lie on the floor, reach my hand in and – 'Jesus fucking Christ!' That's a strong right hook for a one-pawed cat. I'm not surprised he's miserable, the sense of doom and decay here is exhausting. 'That flat he's in,' Terry had said. 'They paid four million for that. Gay couple, work in the City. Only been in it six weeks.' I'd thought if they were gay they might be tidy. My finger is gushing blood. Hold it up above my head – you've got to get it higher than your heart – and race about looking for kitchen towels, which they don't have. Rip off handfuls of toilet tissue. Skid on the way back from the bathroom and realise there's blood all over the poured concrete floor. Wind the tissue a bit tighter, pull on the rubber gloves to hold it in place and start scrubbing the floor with a dish-washing brush in the shape of a cat with bristles on its head. The blood won't come out, although it begins to after about fifteen minutes with some Jif. There's a definite mark though, like a little pink ice rink for ants.

Breathing calmly, start cleaning up Nelson's crap, which fills and surrounds the tray in a decorative pattern; how long has this animal been left? Wee has hardened the granules into rock-like lunar formations. As I pound these with the plastic scoop to loosen the clumps from the sides, my glasses slip down my sweaty nose and fall into the tray. Turning, see that Nelson has come to watch. I can't resent him, that left paw looks very sad in its twisted shape. 'Aw, come on Nelson, old friend.' Reach out tentatively. Nelson puts his head at a crazed

152

angle and swipes again. 'Just missed. Haaaah ha ha ha. One day, you'll be begging.' Although of course it so seldom works that way.

Wash Nelson's bowls, dole out his dry food, his wet food and his water, then wash all the worktop's dishes. But it still smells like a dead body's in the freezer. By the time I leave, feel like I've been in here for weeks myself. Look at Terry's instruction card again. The bit I missed, added later, says, 'Nelson is a Bengal, a muscle ninja. Touch him at your peril.'

＊

On Friday evening I think, that wasn't too bad. I've cycled miles, from Grove Park to Ladywell, I've got a slight sinking feeling, but I've earned £50. I feel dirty but I am dirty. Last cat done, just need a bath. But first, quick look at computer.

Switch it on, wiping cat hairs off my lip, and examine what I'd been doing. Hard to remember the thread. The gallivanting criminals, but what was I about to say, what was the conclusion? Sift through my notes, on the back of Thames Water bills and torn-off bits of the *Standard*. Here we go. I was thinking about how almost all the highwaywomen and most other criminals, and many of the women I've talked about, were so contemptuous of marriage other than for legal benefits, wriggling away from commitment – married life would seem tedious and stifling compared to what they had – and how I admired them for that. I hated commitment myself for years, crazy sexy footloose footpad years, and there's an element of resistance in me still. But do I genuinely want, after all this time, to be a solitary knight of the road?

'Not really.' Hello, Moll. 'And don't glamorise solitude.'

For me it never meant solitude. The reverse – instead of being shut up with one person I had all my girls, just the occasional problematic boy.

She reaches for my rubber hippo and tosses it from hand to hand like a ball. 'I'm the first to advise autonomy. But in

153

case you blocked me out the other day, it's unhealthy to let your feelings fossilise, and the situation's different now. If you're not happy with this man let him find someone else, and maybe choose another one. But how many goes is it going to take?'

She wanders about picking things up and putting them down and then, into a pocket that's deceptively large, she slips something of mine.

Oi, put that back.

'Only doing what you do.'

But I do it with stuff no one's bothered to come back for. Things people probably won't miss.

'You don't even know what you've got. What was...' She moves aside and points behind her. 'There?'

Yes. Right. That broken 1970s metal calendar?

She sighs, and puts down a tiny framed photograph of my mother. Jesus.

'Someone will grab Steve, frankly. You're asking for it. You're absolutely wallowing in spite. So better be sure you won't miss him.'

Pfft. Someone could grab *me*.

She arches a humiliatingly expressive eyebrow.

✳

Monday evening. It's Steve's birthday. He was off in the dark but I gave him his card, and tonight I get back soaked from feeding Oscar, Nelson, no one knows where Houdini's fucking gone and is that my fault?, Maisie, Tinkerbell, Orca, Fred and Ginger in Hither Green where once I'm in I can't get out for some time because the door is swollen by the rain, and Delilah and James in New Cross, all the way in the other direction. Carefully wrap the book I got him. I was going to attempt to make an omelette. Though I'm weird about kitchens because mum was virtually tied to one I can do that, I'm sure. Tidy up, feed my own cats and wait. And then there's a text.

'Can you believe it, Samina's mum's made me a birthday cake. I was quite moved.' Picture of it. Rubbish. 'Her mum turned up here with it, so we're all going for a quick drink. See you later. Thanks for the card, very funny.'

At nine o'clock I just go to bed.

11

Kind of blue

Unleash your voice. Get a megaphone

I was never musical. La Cura Para Del Amor didn't happen in the end. The plan had been that the band strummed shimmering *Paris, Texas*-style slide guitar while I intoned the stories I still tried to find time to write in such a low voice most of the time no one could hear me. I was so crippled by nerves I'd only do it with my back to the audience, and I'd need glasses and a decent light. Once I'd submitted a story plus those demands, the impetus died.

But though I might not have a musical gift, as I got older I could appreciate one. While Maggie was winning every school gymnastic medal in East Sussex, I was closeted in the dark with Cat Stevens, Donovan and Joni Mitchell. I can still sing every track on *Court and Spark*, including 'Twisted', written by jazzer Annie Ross. 'My analyst told me/That I was right out of my head, the way he described it/He said I'd be better dead than live...' The next line is 'I didn't listen to his jive' but of course she does turn out to be schizo. One mental condition that's passed me by, though I could do with the company and seem, with all these voices, to be going through a minor Joan of Arc phase.

My collection is heavy on female singers. Shirley Manson from Garbage. Kate Bush. Courtney Love. PJ Harvey. Amy Winehouse. Liz Phair's articulate roar. Beyoncé, Bessie Smith, and I've got a big weakness for the husky French *je ne sais quoi* not just of Françoise Hardy but also Carla Bruni there I've said it. To name a very few. But look back to the past and you find musicians who made any name at all in a professional sense are usually men or, if women, either educated nuns (Hildegard von Bingen, a sickly child of nobility then an abbess, writer, philosopher, composer) or random gentry – history is thick with classically trained countesses. There must have been working-class troubadour females, so why can't I find them? Because no one wrote about them, presumably. The music gentlewomen penned and performed was so complicated, you'd need a grounding in lute or harpsichord, harmony and counterpoint – but even girls from the educated elite could hit the buffers if they took it all too seriously. Fanny Mendelssohn, sister of Felix, was so gifted that visitors to the family home were as impressed by her as by her brother. But their father was clear, writing to her: 'Music will perhaps become Felix's profession, while for you it can and must only be an ornament in your life'. Felix, that artistic visionary, felt the same. 'Fanny regulates her house, and neither thinks of the public nor of the musical world until her first duties are fulfilled. Publishing would only disturb her in these.' Fanny's, Oh no, I couldn't sit writing music if the floor's dirty. And something in the recycling bin stinks. Where's my Marigolds?

Women who had no money must have made up songs while they turned the fields, as they milked cows. As they cleaned the house. Possibly they sang doing that. They'd improvise lullabies for their babies. Middle-class ladies might sing light opera and a few pious ones did write hymns, because God can always do with a tune wherever it originates. Apart from that, the composing path was upper-class or barricaded. As late as 1880, Chicago music critic George P Upton said in his (presumably short) book *Women in Music* that 'women lacked the innate creativity to compose good music', and this was due to 'biological predisposition'. Good lord, everything these women come up with is *terrible*, okay I haven't heard it

157

but I assume... It wasn't til the Jazz Age, blues, country, music halls then rock and punk, soul-deep sounds that were passionate and confessional, sexy and shirty, that more than a handful of dirt-poor women punched their way out of the sack to write what they wanted to sing and have it recognised. A bit.

But women made music whether or not they wrote it, crooning because they loved to, singing for money because they were ambitious or desperate. Many of these started as or turned into bar-room drunks or hung around playing street corners, and some slipped into the gutter and were never heard of again. Which could've happened to Memphis Minnie.

This room is flooded with a tough, crackly, non-committal voice and a moody, metallic slapped guitar. The magical thing about computers and their robotic insides is they can bring you something so warm and torn. Low-down, urban blues. 'I flagged a train/Didn't have a dime/Tryin' to run away from/That home of mine... didn't know no bettah, oh boy, in my girlish days.' This ain't Muddy Waters swaggering that he's a man, being a man is made easy – it's a woman telling you the simple truth. Minnie was conventionally ladylike unless she thought she'd been dissed, in which case she liked to punch neat and fast; she was red-hot and chilled, with panache and an angular grin like Paula Prentiss or Angela Bassett. I'd do anything to have seen her play.

There's a dispute on location, but most people think Lizzie Douglas was born on 3 June 1897 in Algiers, Louisiana, the biggest ward in New Orleans and the place jazz was born, too. Jutting out on a Mississippi curve, Algiers' first buildings were a gunpowder store and a slaughterhouse – for a while it was known as Slaughterhouse Point, a place of death and killing, but maybe also revolutionary explosions. By the 18th century Algiers was a holding area for imported African slaves who'd survived the hellish voyage across the Caribbean. Swamp gave way to lumber yards, then building on a vast scale. Her parents Abe and Gertrude nicknamed their daughter, the eldest of thirteen, Kid – she couldn't stand her real name. When she was seven, the Douglases moved to Walls, a small farming community twenty miles south of Memphis on Route 61.

In the days before electricity got out to rural areas, music was still homemade; people threw parties or suppers where roast shoat (that's piglet), custard pies and candy sticks dipped in whiskey got danced off by stepping to the shoofly, the scratch and the shimmy-she-wobble.

Shimmy-she-wobble?

'Yeah. It jus' a shimmy, you hold out yo arms and twis' an' shudder yo hips. Get down.'

They banned it as obscene, that's right, I think I read about it. Is this Elizabeth Douglas talking to me?

'Do not call me Elizabeth, honey.'

'Kay. I won't.

'I ain't foolin', so put away that grin.'

No grinning here. I'm smiling. Well, I was.

✳

At seven, Minnie was playing the banjo, broadcasting her tunes. She was trying to copy the syncopated jive of string bands – the ones she'd watch playing for dancers who partied all night and at dawn went straight to working the fields. The monotony and misery of a life spent picking cotton was the reason some workers reached for a guitar instead, though making a living that way was hard enough that they called the thing a 'starvation box'. Could've given that name to my typewriter. Minnie got her first guitar for Christmas at ten or eleven. She'd never wanted to wear her life away as a plantation crop picker or in domestic service. Even at that age, picking guitar at parties, they said she played the instrument 'like a man'.

With a big ego and solid self-belief, a firecracker who couldn't keep still, she started taking off to play around Memphis, and at thirteen ran away from home for the last time, headed for Beale Street. The long Memphis avenue was already a magnet for black travelling musicians. Beale started to fill with clubs, bars and eateries, many owned by African-Americans, and blues players arrived and never left. The Memphis blues was about to be born, and Kid Douglas helped shape it. Scrawny and pretty, she began to get attention as she played with jug bands, who used homemade instruments like spoons and animal bones for drumsticks and bass guitars improvised from a washtub, with a wooden neck and strings. Living in doorways, she played the park and street corners. She was tough, turning out hard, powerful music and frowning a death stare at anyone who looked like trouble.

Itinerant blues musicians would play any venue – work camps, travelling shows, outside of stores. It could be a lonely life, and at a new pitch, especially as a girl, you might not know the local situation and how it could change with just one angry wino. At about eighteen, Minnie got together with Willie Brown, who at fifteen should show her some respect. Brown was older than his years though; he'd been married at eleven, to guitarist Josie Mills, and was already playing and touring through Mississippi. A guitar prodigy who pioneered dark, menacing Delta blues, he turned out solid rhythm and bass lines for the Kid to rip her wild guitar and howl her raucous drone against. They played the resort town of Bedford, where tourists could take the ferry around nearby Lake Cormorant – they'd get on board and entertain the white day-trippers, mixing blues with popular tunes like 'What Makes You Do Me Like You Do Do Do'. 'Why do you try to make me feel so blue, I've done nothing to you...' You can picture her sideways smile. They played dances, store promotions, though guitarist Willie Moore later said Minnie was the better guitarist by far – 'She was a guitar king.'

At twenty, she was offered a job with the Ringling Brothers Circus, and came out of that with a proper act, and knowing she could really make this work. She had a sound and a way about her. *This* is who she was. And as one of thirteen, she wanted and needed to be heard.

Contract up, she returned to Beale – where you still had to be to get recognised. She was a woman now, but Beale Street was tough, and most females who played there didn't make enough to survive, like you so rarely can with something creative. But they could sell their bodies, almost as highly valued as whiskey and cocaine. Minnie had no choice. She got $12 a time – and that was a lot then.

'You think I wanted to do it?'

Obviously not.

'Obviously not.' She sneers and looks out the window. 'You say all this but you don't understand. How come you never had to do that? You strugglin'.' She looks at me. 'Well, you couldn't do it now.'

No.

'Anyway I didn't sing the blues over it. I just got it done.'

✳

There was already a buzz around her because of the way she played, is what makes you want to spit. Most men couldn't

161

play as well but they made more. Still, she whored on her terms as much as anyone could, with a reputation for taking care of herself. Vocalist Johnny Shines remembered, 'Any men fool with her, she'd go for them right away. Guitar, pocket-knife, pistol, anything she got her hands on, she'd use it. Memphis Minnie used to be a hell-cat.'

By my shelves, she picks up a CD case and opens it, taking the disc out to examine. 'It's the only way.'

Sometimes.

'You ever been attacked?'

That's what's so incredible, I haven't. Though I've fought a big man, my dad, to get him off my mother.

She considers me. 'We all done that.'

And you'd actually hit men with your guitar?

'Aw honey, not the good guitar.'

✳

I walked out on Sandy when I thought she'd tried to slap me. I admit I'd been talking, to the magazine's editor, a married man in his early forties with whom it looked pretty clear Madame Defarge was having a thing. I don't know why he'd headed in my direction, I wasn't looking good that day. I had a cold sore, something I never got before Nick gave me his caring gift. Sandy had already noticed my distended lip. When Stuart, the editor, asked how far I'd got with the bound-in *Good Boozer Guide*, I was about to tell him when Sandy trilled, 'I wouldn't stress her. Makes her herpes worse.'

Herpes wasn't well understood back then, but Stuart just raised an eyebrow. I stood up and said, 'I think I'm on top of it,' adding: 'Two-thirds is done.' He nodded. 'Sounds like it's in good shape.' Went to reach for a layout and Sandy said, 'Stu, she's only just touched that.'

I said, 'I'd have to snog Stuart to give him a cold sore.' Stuart said, 'Right, are cold sores and herpes related?' and Sandy marched over and said to me, 'Are you being rude?'

162

The office was at a delirious standstill. I sighed, 'Sandra, that's your job,' she raised her hand, maybe to emphasise a point, but I caught it just in case it was headed for my cheek – so near the herpes! – and moved it away. We were stuck, like a couple frozen on *Strictly Ballroom*, until Stuart said, 'Make sure there's a price guide,' and I said, 'I will', and me and Sandy drifted apart. For ever.

It's odd how after that, I got my groove back completely. I'd heard about a magazine launch, a music, movie and celebrity round-up like a monthly *Time Out*, and talked my way in. The all-female production team was heaven, with a sweet, hip chief sub who played Gregorian chants while we worked. I looked for new writing assignments, which I could do at night, and started stringing for *i-D*, the style quarterly printed on weird thick paper. I interviewed Eartha Kitt, who purred me stories about hanging with Albert Einstein. I met Liza Minnelli and her eyelashes at the Savoy. About this time, too, I got a commission in the 'women's section' of the *Guardian* and met ferocious Diamanda Galás, who'd just written *Masque of the Red Death* for her brother and all the others who were dying of AIDS. The section head changed and I couldn't repeat that, but I learned from Galás. New and ruthless sexual diseases were suddenly everywhere.

But I really did feel like a gladiator who'd fought at least some of them and come out the other side. A regenerating superhero and vampiric daughter of darkness (I'd been bitten but reborn) I typed all night, and though not eating much better took vitamins and cod liver oil. I spent one Christmas Day (bellowed at for helping myself to an apple, presumably the one without the poison, I'd got the last train back from Dad and Deirdre's on Christmas Eve) with Eric, my gay down-stairs neighbour. There was also his lover and his three closest trans buddies, who fussed over me like I was Tiny Tim (the Dickens one). Fairy lights were draped round a reproduction of Michelangelo's David and the table was littered with crackers and diamante jockstraps, which we all put on our heads.

They asked me why I was single, but writing was better than love, even drugs. It gave each day purpose – I could get through anything knowing I'd be sitting at that ancient green Olympia in a pool of evening lamplight or just before dawn, producing a feature against a 9am deadline. Possessed, chortling at my tiny jokes and capturing a side of the person I'd interviewed or the thing I'd researched that no one else had seen, or trying to.

As people passed on their way to work, they'd hear the clatter and the bell of the carriage return and call, 'Morning, Glyn!' It seemed I was singing, pouring out my sound. At that moment and in the words, I could be heard in a way not possible at home, with that throwback's hangups, as he told us to 'lower your voices' and truly did say like a *Monty Python* skit that I should know my place, a bad one because I was common and a girl. And left-handed. 'Never offer someone your left hand to shake. They'll be disgusted.' Now I felt like throwing the sash window wide. 'I'm here! Guess what, I'm left-handed! And I'm shouting my bloody head off.'

*

Minnie liked men, and loved sex. Nearly all her songs are autobiographical; almost all are about making love. Some think she married enigmatic country blues guitarist Casey Bill Weldon in her mid-twenties, she certainly recorded with him. But she definitely got hitched to Joe McCoy in 1929, at thirty-one. Joe could sing, play guitar, and was top notch when it came to jealousy. The photo a few pages back is from a snap of them, Minnie with straightened, Flapper-style hair, lanky in a too-big dress and more than slightly drunk, clutching Joe's padded shoulder for support, and he looks really grim. But they'd been lucky. A Columbia Records talent scout saw them

164

playing for dimes outside a barbershop and flipped. They were shipped to New York, re-christened Kansas Joe and Memphis Minnie and put out a bunch of releases, recording the dirty, rumblin' 'Bumble Bee' two weeks after Minnie's thirty-second birthday. It's the kind of thing Amy Winehouse could get a groove out of. 'Bumble bee, please come back to me... Bumble bee, please come on to me... He got the best old stinger any bumble bee that I ever seen...'

Joe and Minnie took turns to sing on tracks, but Minnie (she didn't mind the new name) had the edge, a knowing, laconic tone matched by lazy finger-clicks. The two moved to Chicago, recording now for Decca. Joe found it harder and harder to bear the centrifugal force of Minnie's growing fame.

No female instrumentalist had ever even dented Chicago's rigorous circuit. But now look. Its king, strutting Big Bill Broonzy, was so pissed off about her audiences, he demanded a blues contest with her. They held it in a nightclub, each singing two numbers, the winner getting a bottle of whiskey and one of gin. Minnie won, with 'Me and My Chauffeur Blues'. Which she wrote. There she is, head back, eyes closed. 'I wants him to drive me, drive me downtown/Yeah, he drives so easy, I can't turn him down... I don't want him ridin' these girls around, so I'm gonna steal me a pistol, shoot my chauffeur down.' Oh mama. Sulking, Bill grabbed the whiskey and sloped off to drink it under a table. Two judges hoisted Minnie onto their shoulders, while Joe snarled, 'Put her down, she can walk.' Of course, Broonzy and Minnie would become the best of friends.

As Minnie's star rose, her marriage to Joe drifted to bits. Soon she was alone. Which, as it turns out, was how she preferred it. Free of encumbrance, she began to experiment. She worked with pianists and drummers, trumpet and mandolin players, and that meant she could concentrate on her voice. She oiled that thing by chewing a wad of tobacco; on stage in

165

a chiffon ball gown, she'd turn sideways and spit a stream of tobacco juice to the floor, foot still tapping her beat. She drank Wild Irish Rose wine, put Copenhagen snuff in her jaw and sucked out its nicotine.

You know I said she had grit? She was beyond fierce, slide guitarist Homesick James testified to it. 'She was real hard to get along with. I mean, she be arguing all the time. "You ain't made that change right, you didn't do this, you didn't do that..." She would always get pissed off about it, the way I played.' She'd have put a perfectionist like James Brown in the shade. 'That woman was tougher than a man.'

But someone saw what was underneath all the self-protection. At forty-two and still a looker she got hitched again, this time to Ernest 'Little Son Joe' Lawlars, three years younger than her and a handsome, relaxed man, smiling calmly in almost every shot I see of him. A guitar player from Memphis, he'd be Minnie's partner for the next twenty-three years. Soulful, fulfilled, occasionally pitch-battle years with a companion who loved and respected her, and some of her best writing comes from then. They performed together and apart; poet Langston Hughes saw Minnie on New Year's Eve 1942 at Chicago's 230 Club, when she was breaking more rules, this time playing an electric guitar that hammered home her barked, yelled, sometimes abusive lyrics.

Writing for the *Chicago Defender*, Hughes opens his review with Minnie sitting on top of a long, low icebox full of beer, accompanied up there by a drummer who 'chews gum in tempo'. She starts to sing, 'hard and strong'. 'The singing, the electric guitar, and the drums are so hard and so loud, amplified as they are by General Electric on top of the icebox, that sometimes the voice, the words and the melody get lost under sheer noise, leaving only the rhythm to come through clear.' This is menacing blues, like no woman I know sings now. Gradually she plays faster, beating her feet, in high-heeled shoes, in time: her toothpick legs 'move like musical pistons'. 'Before she plays she cocks her head on one side like a bird, glances from her place on the box to the crowded bar below, frowns quizzically...'

She's got them where she wants them. She's got life where she wants it. A bottle of wine and she's loosey-goosey enough to become the songs, but not so oiled she's sprawled out and can't focus. Right here she's Memphis Minnie, breaking through, suddenly jerking like a scorpion, grabbing the microphone, yelling, 'Hey now!' Head bowed over it she pounds the guitar, the crowd goes wild and looking up smiling her gold teeth flash, her earrings tremble, her left hand, nails blood red, slides up the strings, her right hand with its big dice-shaped ring picking a throbbing rhythm. This is the noise, says Hughes, of 'Louisiana bayous, Mississippi dust and sun, train whistles in the night, and big rough old Delta cities...'

The sound of what she knows, and the ugliness, lust, regret and elation she's turned into poetry. Music's the lover she loves best. It opens the door, takes her hand, ushers her through to the stage. It's there when she says, I'm a bird of a woman but I can deafen you. You can't help but hear me, and what I say will stay on your mind.

She's been true to this lover, cherished it, protected it, fought for it, and now it does all that for her.

✳

'Siddown. You be tired.'

It's 3am on New Year's Day. Minnie has shoved open the door of their home, at 5300 S. Prairie on Chicago's South Side. She takes off her coat and drops it, goes to the window to glance at the dark, still-noisy street, looks at the bottle at his feet. 'Naw. I can't relax. I'm so tired but I'm jumpy.' Nicotine, booze, exhaustion. Fine New Year, both working different clubs.

He puts down his guitar and moves to her, stroking her thin arms. 'Sure you can. I can help you.'

167

'Yeah? How you gon' do that?' She thinks she knows.

He sits her on the bed. 'Play the song. You not heard it fo' a while. It's 1943 today and this here performance is your new year gift.' He passes her the whiskey and starts to strum the tune he wrote for her, 'Key to the World'.

'The woman I'm now lovin', she is the only one...' Minnie smirks and takes off her shoes, stretching her calves. She watches his handsome head.

'She's a hard-drivin' mama but she treat me nice and kind... A hard-drivin' mama but she treats me nice and kind.' Despite her explosions he knows she's devoted to him. She knows it too. And to show it, once she's taken a drink, she walks over, stroking his cheek. He turns, kisses her hand... And that's about as far as that song gets.

✳

Minnie recorded over two hundred tunes, including some of the regular swing and jazz numbers people also liked – 'I Love you for Sentimental Reasons', 'How High the Moon'. Sweet, schmaltzy songs and so simplistic compared to her own urgent stuff, but she could sing those things because now she knew what they meant. She had fabulous years, playing top-dollar clubs, and at the same time playing to people who couldn't afford to get into clubs. Son and Minnie performed until their health collapsed. At sixty, she had a heart attack. She still tried to play, wouldn't put down her guitar until she couldn't hold it. A committed drinker, she had a stroke, wound up in a wheelchair, and when Joe died of heart disease when she was sixty-four, she crumpled because now she'd lost everything, and had a second stroke. Her sister Daisy moved her to the Jell Nursing Home in Memphis, and when her social security didn't cover the bills, fans sent money to keep her going, and other musicians chipped in. For all her success, she had no cash at all.

It was bad in all kinds of ways. Fans and visitors came to

168

see her, and she wasn't right and she knew it. Musician and civil rights leader Wade Walton paid a visit when she was sixty-five, and her speech was slurred due to the stroke, which embarrassed her. 'I told her we had always loved her records, about "be my chauffeur", and she started to cry.' Blues guitarist Bukka White turned up. 'You know, she got fat as a butterball, that woman did, and all she do is sit in her wheelchair and cry and cry.' You want to stop him just because it's so tough to hear. 'But in her time, she was really something.'

Minnie was seventy-six when she finally gave up, in 1973. She was buried in New Hope Cemetery, Walls, Mississippi, alongside Son Joe, her grave unmarked until, years later, Bonnie Raitt paid for a tombstone.

Maria Muldaur has covered her songs. Jefferson Airplane adapted 'Chauffeur Blues' but didn't acknowledge her original, so she got nothing and at the time she was in the nursing home and could've done with it. Led Zeppelin made a version of 'When the Levee Breaks'; Donovan and Mazzy Star have reinterpreted her stuff. Because it stands up. Because she's a blues guitar hero, an independent woman who came from nothing and worked on the music instead of having kids. The men she married – and there were a lot of men, among them the mysterious 'Squirrel', who she lived with for six years – but the ones she married were the ones who could match her, almost. The ones she could bond with musically, physically and, with Son Joe at long last, emotionally. There wasn't the woe in her songs that you see with Billie Holiday. There was energy, roguishness, honesty and strut.

✳

Don't think about her crying. I don't want to. When there was so much joy that came from a guitar and what you could make it do.

I can hear spectral, cool-buzzin' strumming and a hoodoo voice.

'I been kissin' in the dark, yeah, been kissin' in the dark, Kissin' in the dark, honey that's mah birthmark...'

It fades away and I think how she'd see me, sitting on my own. 'Oh, thass a number 'bout gittin' a sexual disease, sweetheart. Thass no romance.'

It sounds so sassy and funky. I won't say catchy.

' " Got a couple love bumps on mah ding dong". What you think that means?'

Yeah all right. So I know about that.

She snaps her fingers and picks up the song. 'Well, ya better wake up, try to get wise, get yo'self hip to that old crazy jive...'

Clear my throat and she sighs.

'They's all kindsa lyin' and all kindsa heartbreak. And lies you tell yourself.' Glance across the room and picture her, rubbing a woolly-socked foot. 'You not that alone. You a whole woman now, recovered and with a life if you want it, so you oughta remember what yo' missing. How good it feels to share yo'self. And get in bed, I mean *together*. You like it, you know you do.' She winks. 'You been good at it.'

That's how it looks, is it?

✳

Thing about Minnie, she does understand being screwed-up. Looking at the one biography, *Woman with Guitar: Memphis Minnie's Blues*, you stop dead when you read quotes by bluesman Johnny Shines. Here's real temper: 'I heard a lot of things about her. They tell me she shot one old man's arm off, down in Mississippi. Shot his arm off, or cut it off with a hatchet, something.' Anger, maximum resistance to a threat, perceived or otherwise, fucking fuck. And there's more, and that's the point, because even love wouldn't stand in the way of it. 'She'd work Son Joe over right on the bandstand, right in front of the whole audience. Bang, bop, boom, bop! Ha ha.' Funny, yeah. But then Brother John Sellers remembers a time with one of her sidemen, Big Bill. 'Big Bill would never do anything unless'n he called Minnie... And Minnie would always come over because she was big in her heart, even though she could be rough. Blues singers on the South Side can be very tough.'

To conceal any vulnerability she has to come out fighting, or anyway with her fists up. She's leathery. Unbreakable because the breaks of the past have calloused. She ran away from her childhood home repeatedly; why? Saw women taking shit when she lived on the street, and decided to stop doing that herself. She eventually learned to care, in her way, and when Son died she was broken. Sometimes she bullied him, but he stood and took it, let her hammer out her pent-up rage, because he knew why she was like that. She might've been surprised at how deeply she felt about him, a denied, pushed-down love, and only realised when it was too late.

He was her perfect partner, and she still fought with him because she didn't know how else to be.

✳

It's possible I'll never love healthily, of course. Still, sometimes I can trip my baggage as it comes cantering over the horizon. I've decided not to get into a thing about Samina. I always think, offensively, that no one else wants Steve which must be why he's with me, but other women do notice him. I've seen them. Any other man would be tempted to go off with someone more pleasant.

So that night when he got in, I just said happy birthday from under the covers and he said, 'I couldn't get out of it. I didn't want to do that, I wanted to be here.' I thought, 'Yeah...', and then, 'Who knows?' And next evening, I made him the *omelette* as an unbirthday present, and he gave me a big hug, and I said I'd take him to the Dog & Bone at the weekend and frankly the relief of not flying into a rage was uncanny. He probably isn't having an affair, or even thinking about it. Because that might... it might make me have a stroke.

171

I'm travelling miles, feeding cats in East Greenwich, West Greenwich, Blackheath, Brockley, New Cross, Deptford, Charlton, Hither Green, Grove bloody Park. But some of them I'm coming to love. Jane and Mr Rochester, in a stunning West Greenwich Georgian pile. Jane's so pretty, a sweet grey tabby, scampering after Mr Rochester, wanting to play. He glances at her then turns away. They're owned by a Californian couple who make movies and are never in the country. I see more of Jane than they do; she's never going to have any part of her love reciprocated. Then there are Antony and Cleo, two Ragdolls who lollop toward me like Tribbles and drape themselves all over me, they're bred to do it even if they hate you. I sit on the kitchen floor gasping, fur up my nose, deafened by the purring. The owners are young and work in finance at Canary Wharf. There are pictures of them everywhere – her lacrosse team, his rowing team, when both were at Cambridge. A wedding collage covers the entire lower stair area, and everyone is tall and blonde, with patrician features you can't buy. This couple left their Nepal and Tibet itinerary, a guided five-star tour with Cox & Kings, on the kitchen table. When I turned the pages to see the price, I realised you could buy a new car for that. But in the bedroom, where I went to seek out Antony who seemed to be off his food, I saw her note to her husband. 'So sorry, Ratty, that I'm ill every Sunday. We will be on holiday soon! We will come back and not stress about work all weekend! You must stop having stomach aches, too. Love from Otter.' This elite blonde is Otter?

Other cats, in freestyle jungles, want me to come then fuck off. Bojangles, Fifi, Sparkles and Caramel live on Charlton Slopes. When I first opened the door, the stench almost knocked me over. Gagging, I struggled down the hallway past empty Amazon boxes, shoes, muddy bikes and overflowing

172

bags of rubbish. In the kitchen, three trays brimming with cat-shit, six bowls, some upside down. Two pages of instructions. From the sink drainer, next to a radio blaring Capital, Bojangles howled for his Felix Fish Selection, which must be served to him in the upstairs bathroom – where I would apparently find his two bowls and his personal litter tray. I breathed deeply, pulling on my latex gloves.

✳

Pedalling along the A2 in a downpour when my mobile goes. Cursing, stop and drag myself and the bike under a tree, because it could be Terry checking up on me. Wipe the screen dry with my hand and answer.

'Sorry.' Maggie's voice. 'You busy?'

'So-so.' Cars roar past and I try to get the phone under my hood.

'It's Deirdre.' I long to shout, I don't care, but she goes on, 'She's had a stroke.'

Odd, isn't it? You only have to think about a thing and it happens, somewhere on your radar. Inhale wet air. 'When?'

'This morning. She's in hospital. I'd called Dad and was asking about her and he said, She's just been a bit unwell. I said, How unwell?, and without quite explaining he said he'd managed to get her off the floor and onto a chair and she was sitting in it. But not conscious.' She takes a minute, exhausted. 'I had to call an ambulance for them, and she's in an acute ward at the Royal Devon & Exeter. I'm going down there tonight.'

Well, I'm not.

'I've found a nursing home that might take her when she comes out, though Dad's insisting they can carry on as normal.' For Dad, normal is dragging a demented, incontinent woman up and down the stairs to bed to 'save money'. 'Because of her dementia, Sunrise Lodge is going to cost just over £4,000 a month.'

Which is quite a rich irony, really.

'I've looked into their savings and Deirdre's pensions. At the moment, they've got the cash easily. When it gets low, the council will chip in.'

Think of the trouble I've seen, that Dad has never been able to help with. Not that I would ask. Think of the times I've actually sent him money. Sometimes, if you haven't had cash as a kid, you can be quite generous if you have it later. And sometimes not.

✳

The rain is easing. As I push on, see something like an armadillo lying by a lamppost. A soft black leather jacket, so beautiful you can barely touch it – biker-style but collarless, with zips that work. The lining is in shreds, it's been worn a lot, but it remains astonishing. The label says Helmut Lang. And I see from cleaning instructions that the leather is 'lamb'. A lamb. Tragic and innocent. I would never buy this. But. Drape it on a wall so that whoever dropped it will find and rescue it. Gaze at it, as if at an abandoned child, which as a lamb it is. Who could afford something like that? And if you could buy it, and live with its being made of child, who could bear to lose it?

The cats I'm heading to are new ones, Stella and Rocky. Lock the bike and approach the huge house through an immaculate garden. Try the keys. Open one deadbolt, but the second will not turn. The Yale moves, but not the deadbolt. My hand becomes a swollen, macerated mass. Look through the letterbox. Stella, I think it must be, is sitting in the hallway watching. If she could just open the sodding door, this would all be easy. Call Steve at work. 'This new place on Crooms Hill. I can't get in.'

'Well, I don't know what you expect me to do from Croydon. Just calm down. It'll open. It must, obviously.'

Breathe deeply. Rub throbbing hand, flap it about to cool

174

it. Try edging the key in a little less, or ramming it in. Move it sideways. Jiggle it. At long last I see the postman. Beg him to help. Although he's not supposed to do this, he turns the key ('Yes, bit reluctant') and I fall inside. Oh God, but there's an alarm, and it kicks off immediately. What's the code, the code? Normally I would have it ready but the fight for access has emptied my mind. It will be written on the card Terry makes out for every cat. Find it, but I can't see the keypad. Card says, 'Behind bathroom door.' Where's the bathroom? As I sweep the walls the klaxon ratchets to the second level, noise shaking the house as if five copcars are bearing down, which soon they will be. A flash of ginger and Rocky, presumably, races past and is at the open front door when I catch him in a rugby tackle, dragging him screeching and spitting inside and kicking the door with my heel. Wanting to throw up, spot a tiny downstairs cloakroom; yes, a pad on the wall behind a stupid folding door that won't get out of the way and throws the pad into shadow. Key in the four digits. Sudden silence. Collapse against the basin, clutching my chest.

In the barn-like, modernistic kitchen a note gives me instructions. 'Wash and dry bowls before feeding. Rocky has yellow bowl. Hill's Prescription Diet; use measuring cup. Litter trays in second floor bathroom. Every other day, clean and wash them. Hamsters on third floor will need their own food, lettuce strips and carrot batons. Baby hedgehogs on fourth floor need food and clean water. Do not overfeed tropical fish. Vet details below.'

Look around at the anonymous slabs of the kitchen units and start to open them. No sign of cat food, hamster food or hedgehog food. (Terry: 'The hedgehog babies. Sweeeet. But they're hiding in straw, don't try to see 'em yourself. If you let in light, they could go blind.') Look in drawers, fridge, cupboards. Look in the bathroom, in the futility, sorry utility room. From the worktop, framed photos of the family's two

175

kids, Claire and Odile, in their prep school uniforms, simper at me. They get bored with each new pet so fast. Terry told me the girls are getting a python when they get home. Perhaps they're working on an underage twin-sister pole-dance routine?

✳

Ah, raining again. Turn the bike away from the Blackheath uplands and head toward the smoggy Mordor of Deptford. And my favourite of all my charges. At a noisy crossroads just up from Wickes, lock the bike by a burned-out nail parlour, head past the pub where they still have strippers and open a door covered in graffiti. People on the bus are watching; what with my ratty hi-vis jacket, they must think I'm some smackhead. Up stairs reeking of the Chinese takeaway downstairs and unlock what you'd think was a cupboard.

Inside is a bedsit crafted from a cramped pre-war store room. Regarding me amid the roar of juggernauts, sirens and screaming that's coming through the open window is Biskit. Fourteen years old, quite ill really, a mass of matted black fur. Close the door and crouch down, and he descends from his chair, walks across and rubs his head on my leg, purring so that his body reverberates. Biskit's owner is a nurse. Her note is on the sink drainer. 'Dear Terry, Thanks so much for looking after Biskit! I am still not sure if I will go away, he has been very sick again this week.' Glance at him. He gazes up, trustingly, eyes huge golden-brown planets. 'He will need medicine in the purple bottle, 5ml, stirred into his Whiskas. He doesn't like it and he is not eating anyway, so it is difficult.' A drop of sweat rolls off my chin onto the note; the sun's come out and the heat in the bedsit is overwhelming. Two portable fans have been set up to try heaving the air about, but it's still stagnant and rank. The note goes on: 'I am staying in Mallorca. I'll be at this hotel. Please call if he is in any way unwell. PS Help yourself to herbal tea and snacks.' A handful of

176

camomile teabags and a packet of Budgens flapjacks by the note. In the bathroom, which is part of this room but separated by plasterboard and so noisy it seems to be perched on a bridge above a motorway, there's a pool of stinking vomit by the toilet. Start to clean it up and find Biskit at my elbow, frowning with apology.

Wash his bowls, put in the food and meds, and he examines the mixture before walking away. 'You've got to eat, pal.' Sigh, sink down on the sofa, and Biskit curls onto my lap. Stroke him, feeling how little there is of him. We sit together, breathing, thinking, as another row erupts outside the pub.

✴

But every morning I'm up early trying to write. Is it awful? Probably. But I'm doing it. Instead of interviewing other people and telling their story to sell their album, or pushing pet insurance that will find some way not to pay out. I've never said what I really have to say. As I put down the words, feel my soul expand.

✴

After the storms, the jacket looks very wet. Aren't they coming back?

✴

Friday at the Dog & Bone. And I really am feeling better. Mentally lighter, shoulders less hunched with lamentation. Take off the butcher boy cap I wear on the bike and Steve smiles. 'You look fabulous.' I do? Well, that's because I've got regular income, but I've also proved I can manage on less; things I thought I needed, I don't need. Regular cycling makes me feel fitter and I'm working on my thing. Shrug off the leather jacket. Yes. But it'd been there a week. It fits me as if it knows me.

A track comes on and I snap my fingers and croon along, not even thinking what it is. 'Baby, baby, baby don't leave me... Ooh please don't leave me, all by myself...' I haven't sung

177

in ages. 'You came into my heart (baby, baby) so tenderly/With a burning love, that stings like a bee...' Wag my finger, miming. Then his mobile goes.

Samina. Of course.

✳

Six at night, and I open the door to Biskit's. I may be fitter, but doing quite a physical job is harder when you're older. Bit of a shock to feel just how much older.

Biskit has diarrhoea, and I see with a sinking heart he's thrown up again. He smiles at me, a captive in this boiling prison and with no outside access, but loved, deeply loved by his owner. I clean his bowls, seeing he's eaten nothing. And then I think, if I could get his liquid meds down him we'd know he'd had them, and they wouldn't be making his food taste bad. Cradle Biskit, open his jaws and squirt the syringe down his throat. Put him on the floor, go to fill his water bowl, glance back, and a nightmare is unfolding. He's walking in reverse, foaming at the mouth so badly it looks like pints of yellow vomit. Fool, fool. Sweep him into the bathroom and rinse water into his mouth. He struggles. And then the foaming stops. Biskit is soaked. Sit on the floor with him, stroking him as our hearts pound.

When we're calmer, feed him, watching like a hawk. And he does at least eat something, despite my attempt to kill him. While he snuffles in his bowl, look at the birthday cards on the shelves. 'Happy 40th to the best daughter in the world. All my love, Mum.' I assumed younger than that.

'Life begins at 40, Gill!'

'Happy birthday, Gillian. So pleased you're enjoying London. Your cottage sounds sweet. You've had so much heartbreak, we're relieved to see you settled and hear you're both so happy. Don't go too mad living the high life down there! Love to you and Biskit from Auntie Jan and Uncle Vern.'

Sit on the hair-encrusted sofa and pat my lap. Biskit trots over, tries to jump up, can't, and I carefully lift him. I smell of vomit and cat shit but he doesn't mind because he does too. And also, if I bury my nose in his fluffy head, of warm biscuits. Smooth his fur and softly sing him made-up lullabies until, exhausted, and despite armageddon outside, we both fall asleep.

12

Untitled #2

However ugly things look, if you want, you can see beauty

I'm at a bohemian London members club. I've never been here before and it's a pretty dude-y joint – low-ceilinged, with twisting corridors and a wooden-galleried bar. I expected to feel out of place but I don't, though I thought twice what to wear (racer-back dress, biker boots and the jacket). The club members are nonconformists, they don't care if they look 'right' and so of course they do, they look beautiful, man, and they all seem humorous and kind. It's like a prettier version of the Dog with more cash and less entertaining jokes.

I'm here for the reunion of a middlebrow news magazine, let's call it the *Post*; our picture editor, James, once the debonair office Romeo, is a member. It's twenty years since I worked with this crew and a few I haven't seen in the interim. Two of us have died of cancer, some have lost weight, unexpected ones have put it on, and I've changed in more ways than just two new tattoos.

I found myself, when I first arrived, in quite an intense conversation. I'd been explaining something to two friends, one once very close, one now a broadsheet editor.

'What?'

The editor leaned across and in a calm voice repeated to my other pal what I'd said: 'Donor eggs.'

I mean, you may have seen this coming. I feel certain it's not news to you. But it is to the friend. As they considered me, horrified and caring, for what seemed ages, I looked round the big circular table. When we worked together, almost all

180

these women were happily married or about to be, and I was in thrilling, occasionally degrading romantic turmoil. Now most of them are divorced, or their husbands are cheating on them and from the gossip only some of them know. The editor, one of the first women I knew to publicly come out, is on dating app Her and has been telling us about her exploits, week-ends in Paris, Seville, Reykjavik, where she and the girl don't even leave the room, which seems a shame. This woman's two years the other side of menopause, and the one-time studious problem-page writer has jettisoned her dark bob cut and Belfast wanness for long magenta hair and skin like a Cuban goddess. There is no sense of her being over thirty-five. Still, there's a blizzard in her glance like a storm off the Malin Head.

'All the women I'm meeting are ultimately fucking bores. Or boring fucks.' That's what she'd said, eviscerating a bread roll. 'Not one is as sexy or clever as my ex.' Her Italian wife was – well, is – eight years younger than her. She took her eye off the ball when her career went stratospheric, and a girl at her partner's casting agency made a play for Sophia when my friend was heading up her paper's Manchester office. The girl's ten years younger than Sophia – she's forty-seven, her new woman is thirty-seven. The couple have year-old twins. My pal could be the twins' grandmother. She still loves Sophia.

'But you're shagging them anyway?' I'd asked, intrigued. Where did she find the libido? This led to relating the dis-appearance of mine, and explaining – briefly, briefly – the medical background to how I got where I'm at.

The more intimate of my two listeners saves me in the post-donor egg silence. 'So what's Steve doing today,' she smiles, 'while you're here?'

I don't want to say, working on a Saturday catching up on bid-writing because the company's backed up due to wholesale sackings. Working with this girl Samina. Instead I tell them what he's planning later. 'Doing the weekly shop. Then attempting to put up a curtain rail.' Unless he and the woman I'm obsessed with go for a drink. Saturday. Why wouldn't they?

'I just can't believe you've finally got a decent guy.' This from the broadsheet editor. Nod. Shake my head. 'He's a lot younger than me.' Dunno why I said that.

Her expression is arctic. Force nine off the starboard bow. 'And he's good?'

The other friend, who once met him, beams: 'He's lovely.'

The very table has frozen to a block of ice. I see regret under that tan, and brittle misery. And I understand her feelings, no one could grasp them more.

'I'm pleased for you. But I'm... shocked. Almost unbelievable, really. That you're the one who's happily settled.'

✳

When we're packing up, and some of us are leaving but not the editor, she's in for the long haul, retiring to the bar itself, she puts her cheek to mine and says, 'How lucky we haven't bumped into that clubby artist you had just before you came to the *Post*. Boy, did he sound unhinged. Piss artist!'

Give her a rueful smile. And she never heard the full story of that one, either.

Reeking of booze but handling it, she grabs her bag. 'You've had 'em all, kid. Ever had a waiter?'

Not that I... But she's gone, strolling in the same direction as the long-haired waitress. Wonder how much top-class, Harley Street HRT she's on.

✳

Unless you were a caveman, you won't be surprised to learn, doing art wasn't a working-class thing for a long, long time, and even when it was, it wasn't a working-class female thing. You were so not going to get something like Young British Artists, most of whom knew they had to shock and market themselves aggressively to sell because they needed money. Look at

182

Tracey Emin. Haunted, inventive. Part Turkish-Cypriot, born in Croydon, brought up in Margate where she was raped at thirteen, went to Medway College of Design, met Billy Childish and they plunged into confrontational imagery of the sort that would be either dismissed or get just the attention they needed. Emin's nothing if not driven. In a 2014 *Guardian* interview, she said, 'Work is good. If I don't make things, I become ill and depressed. Painting makes me feel like a better human being.' She says she's not ambitious but she is. 'I recognised opportunities; I wasn't afraid and I took risks.'

The history of women painters. There was some sort of unisex vase decorating in ancient Greece, but you can paint a vase in the Wedgwood factory. Medieval female artists were as usual aristocrats or nuns, generally again at the same time. During the Renaissance they were rich too, or the privileged daughters of artists; baroque era, ditto. And so on, all charming and refined. And then we get Suzanne Valadon.

The boy here is Maurice Utrillo, the French painter who drank himself to death. He never knew if his father was Spanish exhibitionist Miguel, who donated his surname, or Degas or the postman, all his mother's lovers. Doesn't matter. He was the son of Valadon, who taught him. None of his work, which is bleak, almost monotone, almost nondescript, has the savage power of what his mother produced. I may be one of the few who think this. But Maurice paints bare street scenes, featureless landscapes. Valadon paints women: crying, grinning, washing, working – shocking her audience with the frank, primitive look of her girls and colours that knock your eye out. She painted men and women in love and naked together, something no one had done. Her women's stares and pissed-off triumph remind you of Paula Rego's surrealism and ugly confrontations. People frowned; were women really like her women? Then they heard about Valadon's gonzo existence, so like a man's, and were disgusted. I think she and Emin could've been friends.

She was born Marie-Clémentine Valadon on 23 September, 1865 in the small town of Bessines-sur-Gartempe in western France. Her mother worked at the Auberge Guimbaud, doing the hotel's laundry, cleaning and mending. There was real stigma in being an unmarried mother in a narrow-minded community, and Madeleine, bad-tempered at the best of times, drank hard. When Marie was five, Madeleine had had enough of the bigotry and relocated them to Paris. She could just afford a room in dirt-cheap Montmartre, with its cramped old houses, pimps, whores and painters.

Valadon jnr loves it. She goes native, roaming the streets when her mother's at work, scaling fences, dangling off balconies like a monkey. She chats to strangers, picking up filthy language and songs, which she bellows loudly, a total showboater.

And she's drawing. By the time she's eight their room is littered with stick-figure images on scraps of paper. One afternoon she watches a painter in the rue Lepic. 'Don't give up, pal. You're not bad, yeah?' Pierre-August Renoir, white as a sheet, hair a lank tangle, turns. At thirty-five he looks like a young Viggo Mortensen.

'Well, I'll treasure that.'

He'll be famous soon, then people will start to call his Impressionism simplistic, though it will last and last. For now he smiles. Christ, she's tiny though. Is she stunted? There are scabs on her legs and she stinks. Unlikely he would expect one day to be the lover of this unhygienic dirtbox.

It's not just Madeleine and her daughter who have nothing. The Franco-Prussian war means the Germans have closed Paris down. With no food, people fight over horses, dogs, rats.

A convent school just steps away is offering free classes. Monkey-girl is sent to the nuns, but they decide Marie-Clémentine – let's call her Suzanne now, that's the name she'll use soon – is a deviant. The pauper girls are told to learn from the middle classes and be moderate in all they do, but every word she scrawls is crazed, emotional and untidy. Each evening she picks flowers for Madeleine, or awaiting her re-turn draws her pictures of posies, horses, cats. Madeleine is indifferent. And when Suzanne draws naked figures, she goes haywire. If she's not pulverising her child, Madeleine doesn't touch her.

But beyond the room, Paris is becoming calmer. The Third Republic now rules France in some almost capable way. Artists who'd fled the city's hysteria return to Montmartre, sculptors, painters, writers, actors living in stables or lofts, filling the lanes with energy. Anywhere else, Suzanne would be head-ing for working the streets and an early death but here, if you're creative, there's a chance. At nine years old she kicks around cafes and bars at night, the Moulin Rouge, the Chat Noir, staring from the shadows, and the people passing on their way to drink and talk all night include Renoir, Monet, Degas, Cézanne, Seurat, all unknown. Most are wealthy or middle class, but still possessed with a need to make it. She recognises that hell-bent restlessness, but for them it's allowed. According to John Storm's long-out-of-print biography of her,

The Valadon Drama, as a child Suzanne never seriously considered the idea of being an artist, she expected drudge work. It was just so good to see these weirdos, she'd never found anyone like herself before. 'Pierre, isn't that the kid that keeps bugging you? Ah, she's gone. Right – bottle, jug?'

✳

No time for painting now, though; she's apprenticed at a sweat-shop in the Place de Clichy, little girls packed into an airless workroom. Next, she's a waitress and dishwasher, then works in a livery stable. The horses trust her, let her do handstands on their backs, then headstands, then somersaults. Which leads to work at a run-down circus in the suburbs.

Only she offers to stand in when the trapeze artist is ill. At sixteen, monkey-girl actually has been on the trapeze, but she's not as tough as she thinks and she's not professional. Sweating, shivering in her tatty rhinestone outfit, standing high on the platform, looking down. 'It's impossible I can't do this. I am a cat. I fly and climb.' The mad carney band, the drum roll. She smoothes the corset with the little fringe. Grabs the tra-peze as it flies toward her. She's up! It's easy! She nearly laughs as she hurtles through the spotlight's dazzle, legs curved to-gether and hooking onto the rail, jumping to the platform. A flirty bow, grips the trapeze, leaps again, through the moonlight of the spotlight, the second trapeze coming, misses it.

Seems to drift, suspended in mid-air. No net, smashes into the ground.

✳

One day the editor of *i-D*, on whom I had a crush the size of the Eiffel Tower, suggested I try writing fiction. I don't *think* it was a swipe at my accuracy. He said he'd seen imagination in my stuff, thought I could do more.

You know how sometimes it doesn't occur to seriously try your fantasy thing until someone says they believe you can? It was like he'd given me the keys to a Merc and told me to take it for a spin. Luckily it didn't cross my mind that I'd failed my driving test. So I tried, picking up where I'd stopped, though of course I hadn't really ever, completely. At night I'd get in from work, feed the cats, break open a fresh pack of Dunhill and rev up the typewriter.

Banging out tales of London life and magic realist weirdness, I was ripping my years of desk-bound fact-checking to shreds, coming up with things from my head, and the more unzipped they were, the better I liked it.

✳

After the accident, Suzanne was finished as a performer. Until her damaged back had healed and she could look for other work, she followed a friend's suggestion to model. She turned up at the fountain in the Place Pigalle, where each day hopefuls of all shapes, sizes and sexes paraded, trying to catch an artist's eye. The artists' eyes practically fell out of their heads. They hadn't seen this amazing-looking girl – elfin, dark eyes, pillowy lips – since she was a bag of rags.

They fought over her and, posing in an artist's studio, she realised she'd found her way into that world she'd been obsessed with. She got dragged to bars, or they all had dinner in a cheap bistro, paid for by whoever sold a painting, and she joined in the discussions, laughing, arguing her point.

But better than that, Suzanne was analysing how each artist worked. How they studied her, then transferred what they saw to the canvas. She began to draw again and now her figures were fluid. She still used strong, brutal lines, but there was control and expression. And a lot of herself, her need and intensity. Every other painter on the scene had had tuition, even the group's few women – Marie Laurencin, Berthe Morisot, Rosa Bonheur – were rich and had studied art, often tutored abroad. No one guided Suzanne, and she didn't expect it. She kept her work inside the apartment. It was a secret.

✳

'Zis fing wasn't hard to do.' Obviously, there's a tiny woman in here. Tiny and outlandishly lovely. 'I draw what I know, a child who combs her hair, flowers, fings that give me pleasure. And I worked like mad. Why are you doing zis offensive phonetic rendering of my speech?' I don't know. Sorry. Really childish, goes back to the De la Moule business. Dad. Habit. Will stop.

✳

Suzanne was also in the middle of a sea of lust. Montmartre seemed to exist in dramas of passion, it was how the artists operated. At sixteen she was screwing constantly. Waiters, postmen, sailors. Be good to see her version of Tracey Emin's Everyone I Have Ever Slept With 1963-1995.

Part of this pheromone-sozzled world was Miguel Utrillo, a Catalan engineering student. He hung out with his coterie at the back of the Chat Noir, drinking cheap cognac. The group includes – oh, this is like watching Woody Allen's *Midnight in Paris* – Paul Verlaine, who would drunkenly read out his poems; Sarah Bernhardt, delivering Shakespeare; Guy de Maupassant sharing stories in progress; Claude Debussy, presumably humming. Utrillo wasn't a real artist but he acted like one, giving a lecture on Spanish dance from on top of a table, riding a donkey into a club. Suzanne started spending time with him; he wasn't bad looking, stagily eccentric in the way someone who wants to look eccentric and has the money to do it might be. When people noticed she was pregnant, one taxi-carriage driver shrugged and said, 'The little one is bitten at last? But which mosquito bit her?'

13

I'm not blaming Charlie, you couldn't, but she invited herself to an Indian place in Stokey and brought a puppyish young artist. We all had dinner, me in my good old scuffed catsuit and sneakers, Charles in torn biker lycra and Mexican beads and this boy in a really stupid jacket I discovered was what his artistic friends wore, with uneven lapels. He looked like he'd just climbed out of a toybox, but he was sweet and funny and clever and very good looking. Adam invited me to Spitalfields market for the following weekend, which in those days when Shoreditch was still bleak began at around 6am and was not the manufactured mall it is today. On the way back, since he lived not far from me, we had a drink by the River Lea, and when I got home the phone rang. 'I have to tell you I can't see you just as a friend. Can we be more than that?'

It revved up fast, because that's how he did things, like a kid on a helter-skelter. I couldn't get into it at first, he seemed so... childish, although knowing at the same time. Anything wrong for me and he'd put his arms round me and say into my hair, 'What is it? Tell uncle Addie.' My Stokey friends accepted him into the group and he was shocked at the greaser style we had because we didn't have the cash he could splash. He began to copy the *Easy Rider* look, buying the black drainpipes that, at twenty-two, he should've been wearing. Nine years younger than me. Good Christ, that was *too many* years younger. Having coffee on Sicilian Avenue, Charlie grinned, 'I've never seen him like this.'

'Like what?'

'He's gone ape. You're all he talks about.'

'I don't know if I want him. He's just... He's so...'

'Pretty.'
'That, too.'

✳

The sex was terrible. Naked, he seemed like a puppet, head huge on his Pinocchio body. His cultivated parents came one time. His mother didn't seem much older than me.

At a housewarming for his flat in gunslinging Dalston, one of his female friends asked me, unsmiling, 'How old are you?' He heard it, stroked the side of my face while De La Soul sang 'The Magic Number'. Murmured, 'You don't have to like all my friends. I don't like some of 'em myself.' I started to fall for him.

As I waited outside Beigel Bake, he chucked my bagged-up order through the door to me. 'Here y'are, sexy! Catch!' Awkward. Endearing. He's still learning.

He flew to New York, where he shared a flat and studio and had an agent. Letters arrived, pouring out news and love ('I even miss the railings outside your flat...'), with intricate illustrations of us flying through the sky together, riding dolphins in tropical seas. He begged me to visit for a week and I did – he swooped at me at JFK arrivals like some mad bat, trembling with anticipation. And though he left me on my own during the day for six days while he worked, at the end of it, for his birthday, we went to an Alphabet City party held for him by an artist couple. A baritone just off stage at the Met sang him 'Happy Birthday'. He was younger than anyone there. 'He's a prodigy,' someone told me.

At a glitzy opening, everyone coked out of their minds, I wandered round looking for him. He was being feted like a star. In one of his paintings, a little girl lay spread on a bed, naked but for shoes, genitals lovingly detailed.

He bought me tequila to make sex better, but halfway through stopped and said, 'You're not even wet. I can't work with this.' Joking because he thought he wasn't enough of a turn-on? What was my problem? On the last day he said, 'Our sex has improved.' I nodded, smiling. News to me.

Back at the listings magazine where I still worked then, a bouquet of unearthly flowers arrived at my desk. The card (he must've faxed the design to the florist) showed a woman's curvy arse with a fox's brush, because I'd said I'd like a tail. My phone rang. As if he was psychic and in a voice so huskily hushed he could've been next door, not next door to the Guggenheim, he said, 'I want to be your husband.' I didn't know what to say so I said, 'Come over here and say that.'

And in a week or two he did.

My God, said friends who met him. He. Is. A. Dream. He adores you, he's so full of energy and humour, the way he *looks* at you. You're so lucky.

✳

When people suggested various fathers, she'd say, 'It could be,' or 'I hope so.' Toward the end she was too big to work, but even though Madeleine had lost the jobs she'd got and Suzanne had been earning for them both she seemed to have money, presumably from whoever thought he was the man. At noon on 26 December, a jaundiced little boy was born, bruised by forceps. The three of them moved from their room in the grubby rue du Poteau to a serene apartment at 7 rue Tourlaque, close to the Sacre Coeur. There was a nurse, too, for tiny Maurice. At eighteen, Suzanne was as careless a mother as her own had been. She was at parties, dance halls, cabarets. Men wanted her again and she loved that. Miguel Utrillo was almost always at her side. Perhaps she's played a blinder to make sure she'll never be hungry again. His studies over, Miguel heads to Bulgaria, then Germany. The only person who always knows where he is is Suzanne.

✳

And then... 'Renoir fell in love wiff me. He was madly in love.'

He was. Renoir was still Hollywood-attractive. He painted

Suzanne, no longer the stinking waif, in Le Bal a Bougival, and you know which one in that painting she is – the girl who holds your attention, with an auburn fringe and a red bonnet and a man swirling her and desperate to kiss her.

''E was a total romantic.' Suzanne is walking round my room, hands brushing surfaces then stroking her neck in an annoying, posturing way. How old is she when she's here? Fifties? My age? The age where things begin to go wrong and you act like a preening dork fantasising about your youth?

'I was in love too.' She looks at me in a friendly way. ''E was courting me. We walked togezzer. You carn't kip making out zat I speak like dis.'

Well, you do but never mind.

'But why must you make me a figure of fern?'

Because maybe I'm the heartless one, and I need a laugh. You'll see.

'So... every girl envy me. He take me to Guernsey. And when we there, he receive word from his woman, Aline Charigot, who I didn't know about. And that is that.'

But before he kicked her out, he'd seen her work, one day when he called on her without warning. 'You too? And you hide this talent?' He never mentioned her work again, and it hurt. And then she thought about how easily she could draw dynamic lines, and how Renoir laboured over his technique. She began to wonder if he didn't mention her work because... might he truly think it was good?

✳

'What's all this, foxy?'

Adam had arrived at my flat one night out of the blue, hammering on the door. 'You writing something? Feature?' He ripped the paper out of my typewriter so hard he nearly damaged the platen. I tried to grab the page but he held it over my head. 'Looky here. Unbelievable! "I am a fox. Or if not a fox, a wild thing..."'

192

He put it behind his back. 'So. Writing fiction...' I wasn't sure about the tone. Adam wrote illustrated fiction, for children. They were sweet tales.

'Can I have that back?'

'I bet there's more. Is there more?'

He was hunting through my desk, then under my circular side table. 'Found it, you little squirrel. Who's been a busy squirrel?'

He dragged out the cardboard box filled with stories, hunkered down, began to riffle through. 'Yeah, had to be doing this. Creative dreams, I guess.'

'Adam, give me that page. Now.'

He looked up with a wide, boyish smile. 'Well, make it work for you. Send it to publishers. Monetise it!'

'Eventually. I'm still practising, really.'

'Right now. You're getting older. Don't waste time.'

The 'getting older' bit surprised me.

✳

I did what he said, sent three stories I'd honed to four publishers I respected. Two liked the work but couldn't go further, one wanted me to go in for a chat and the fourth – said they wanted to publish a collection, and could I send everything I had?

But I didn't have my shit together. I had things that maybe had potential, but... I tried to quickly edit a dozen and sent them. Polite rejection note.

On the phone, rushing between appointments, Adam said, 'Forget those publishers, they know you now, they've written you off. Do something else. Write a play.'

I'd loved working on those stories, but I'd exposed them and they'd been found lacking. Feeling I'd lost my true companion, writing, I went round to Adam's more and got clinging. In the Bucks Head in Camden, surrounded by the Stokey posse, he said, 'When we getting married?' I wondered if he wanted that so much because I hadn't said yes. Or because I was sort of creative but not like him. 'I'll wear a Nick Cave jacket and a greasy tie.' My mates were looking over, the blokes grinning. He stood up. 'Marry me!'

I climbed over the back of the seat and went to the toilet. I sat looking at the graffiti for a while and when I came out, Adam was with two of my closest male friends, arms round their shoulders. He was becoming part of my group, taking it over from me, making it his.

✳

In the spring of 1887 someone moved into a studio on the top floor of Suzanne's building, an artist her age, twenty-two. Descended from viscounts, Henri de Toulouse-Lautrec was wildly wealthy. At fourteen, he'd slipped on a polished floor and broken his left leg; a year later he cracked the right. With twisted, frail limbs he's supposed to have been ugly but he's not: olive skin, sympathetic eyes, exotic and seductive.

His personality was upbeat, buoyant, and this studio at the rue Tourlaque was where Montmartre's most engaging play-wrights, journalists, art dealers and singers came together. His friend Suzanne was soon the unofficial hostess, a kindred spirit, a rebel who couldn't stand convention.

And then he knocked on her door to ask her to a party and found her drawing. He was so impressed with the work he forgot his party, perching on a chair to watch. He began to encourage her. He bought her work, hung it in his flat and challenged friends to tell him the artist. Degas? Rodin?

He asked her opinion on his works in progress. Soon they were sketching together, critiquing each other's art, then both, despite the other's protests, throwing the drawings dramatically on the fire.

Suzanne sat for him, most notably for The Hangover – sprawled at a café table, sulking.

It was he who said it. Change your name to Suzanne.

194

*

I've got Leonard Cohen's song on my mind.

'Now, Suzanne takes your hand and she leads you to the river/She's wearing rags and feathers from Salvation Army counters/And you know that she will trust you...'

In the song Suzanne's half crazy, and the singer has 'no love to give her', so it doesn't apply to Valadon, does it? Though something about it's familiar.

*

Another bouquet arrives – spikes, strange flowers reaching out to do a surreal kind of damage. The cool women I work with love it, though when I find a bucket big enough for the blossoms, the girl next to me mimes puking into it with envy. Ho ho. Fill it with water, put in the spiked monsters, pushing their spiteful arms away from my neck.

They've all heard about my failed publishing effort, and someone mentions a creative writing course. It's a new thing. Go on, try. There's an MA only, you need a BA to apply. I fill in the forms, write a letter about why I don't have a first degree, then post the lot, with those original stories.

I haven't told Adam, can't stand more shame. We have a bath together at his huge, bare flat, candles flaring on the washbasin, the *Brandenburg Concertos* deafening. He stands us in front of his flyblown mirror. Adam is growing, developing. Becoming handsome. 'Look at us. We'd have incredible children.' That's so vain. 'What's the matter?' he says, irritated that I'm not posing too, or drinking whiskey from the bottle. 'What you need is a good, hard fuck.'

Another bouquet, spiralling but spindly. 'They're getting smaller, Glyn,' someone laughs.

*

Lautrec told Suzanne to show her work to Degas, regarded as the master. Degas went through the portfolio then slowly turned to her: 'You're one of us.' Degas made her his friend.

195

He'd never met someone like Suzanne, a guttersnipe who said what she felt and regaled him with tales of the street. He stared at her work, its vivid fervour.

She kept at it. Her paintings appeared at exhibitions. She had a one-woman show. She saw the work of Gauguin and the similarity in their styles. Galleries took her studies, prints sold. She painted blue-collar women washing themselves in basins in the cold, men as objects of desire and earthy female nudes, something women weren't supposed to depict because only men did that.

✳

I got offered a place on this prestigious course. I rented out my flat and moved, with a few boxes of belongings and my two cats, into Adam's until it was time to head to Norfolk. The thing that was wrong got worse.

'When I said do something creative, I didn't mean live in some shithole in the country.' He threw that over his shoulder one morning before I left for work. When I got back, he wasn't there. I roamed the apartment, staring at the dismembered dolls hanging from walls. I found a series of paintings, some still wet, ferocious fanged fantasy animals that seemed to want to tear me apart if they could just get through the canvas. The phone rang and it was a mate, a bloke I'd always trusted. 'Just seen Adam, in the Wheatsheaf with his hand on some woman's thigh. Assume you two are okay?'

A one-legged doll was smirking at me with her painted-on Droog face. I told her, 'Just fuck off', hung her in the hallway, then closed the door in case she could hop.

✳

Wealthy banker Paul Mousis; one evening, he finds himself in the spinning world of artistic Montmartre. Who is that – *who* is that stunning dark girl?

Mousis is not unattractive. Obsessed with Suzanne, he's always there, throwing money down even if what they're doing seems pointless to him. She can't help but reciprocate. He builds a country home in Montmagny, 25km north of Paris, telling her that to develop her art, she should leave distracting Montmartre. They go – Mousis, Suzanne, troubled Maurice and Madeleine, who surprisingly spoils her grandson. When Maurice has his fits of rage, she gives him soups laced with wine.

Suzanne has a big house to run, and soon there's no time to paint. And then Maurice goes batshit. He starts disappearing, usually to be found in a ditch. A gangling teenager, he gives in to his alcoholism and smashes rooms to pieces, or craps on the stairs. In the sanatorium Mousis pays for, he's given paints. From the start, his work is formidable.

Suzanne returns to her Montmartre studio and embarks on a breakthrough series of drawings, channelling the guilt of her neglect of her son by using her body as a naked model. She moves Maurice to the centre of her world and puts painting back there too. Once again, she feels fully alive.

✳

I was in love by then, that's the predictable bit, because despite it all there was still the tender, bear-cub side of him. I was invited to a party at *i-D*; I'd won a surprise award. I got back from a day blasting my mind out at *Prima* and started to get changed.

'Come in here.'

I walked to the front room. Adam grinned. 'I don't love you any more.' The grin widened. 'You need to move out tonight.'

I said, 'Why?' He shrugged. 'Grown out of it. And I never could stand fucking Nick Cave.'

So I missed the *i-D* party. I was in a cab with my cats in their boxes, headed to one of a series of friends' places where I'd crash until term started, so I could stay in London and earn to the last minute. 'I allergic to cat!' yelled the driver, lighting

197

up, blowing smoke back at us like it could overwhelm the dan-
der, turning his Turkish rock to the max.

✳

A month later, I was living in an unfurnished boathouse with
storage heaters that didn't work. When the van my mate had
rented to help me move dwindled at the end of the road and
turned the corner, silence fell. No sirens, no car boomboxes,
no singing from the street. Suburbia. I bought a futon mattress
from Ikea and lugged it through the cobbled streets. The
caretaker found a desk in the garage and I cleaned it, put my
faithful Olympia on it and pulled on my fingerless gloves.

✳

'Don't you even prepare your canvas?' Maurice, back in
Montmartre near his mother, is painting. He looks up and
there is an Adonis, blonde stubble, humorous mouth, in which
is a pipe. André Utter is twenty-two to Maurice's twenty-five,
an artist, son of a plumber.

'They would paint together, André talking about his
philosophy of life.'

And you were, at this time..?

'Forty-three. 'E saw me one day passing in ze street – must
we kip zis up?'

I'm quarter French Canadian. Maybe an element of self hate.

'And he couldn't beliff it.' Suddenly she's that age again.
'Neat, curving body. Beautiful breasts.' Cups them. 'He fan-
tasise about me, no idea that I am the mother to Maurice.'

When he finds out, he's surprised but it doesn't put him
off. She asks him to pose for a raunchy painting, Adam and
Eve, and halfway through that – because did Adam wear
clothes? – they get it on.

She breaks off with her banker and finds a bigger studio,
moving there with Utter, her sheepdog, two tomcats and a goat
only too happy to eat her bad drawings. They live on the sale
of their pictures. Friends, painters, writers turn up, someone

198

gets out a fiddle, someone starts a discussion about play of light and, later, Suzanne and Utter fall into bed. She stinks of oil paint, pastel and chalk dust, it's in her hair, on her nose. She looks twenty-five.

The rattan chair behind me, salvaged from a Blackheath skip, creaks now as someone drops into it. She runs a hand through her hair. It's short, in a square greying bob that shows her sagging jowls. 'Such tender lips. Hard, ingenious hips, and mine were the same.' In her sixties maybe, she's been reading over my shoulder. She shakes her head, rubs a hair sprouting from her chin with a finger, dried paint under the nail, and I pass her the tweezers.

'I was so 'appy.'

I know you were.

✳

So I went to classes and met the really bright people on the course, and I pounded away and got called a 'ghetto writer' (because I wrote about London) by a refined Dubliner whose stories concerned his Jesuit school – again and again and again – and then I got a call. Adam, at Liverpool Street. 'I'm a fool. I'm coming, whether you like it or not.' Two hours later I opened the door and he was on his knees. I was so happy. We went for dinner at an Indian place where he stole handfuls of cutlery because I didn't have any.

✳

Suzanne and Utter paint all day. Years go by. Maurice's work starts to really sell, and at this point the 1914 war begins. Utter, twenty-eight, enlists, and she watches as his train leaves, her golden boy surrounded by other young soldiers. She trudges home from the Gare Montparnasse, her forty-nine years dropping round her like chains. He'd insisted on marrying her before he left, and she decides to astound him when he returns with how young and fabulous she is, how men desire her. She starts to behave ludicrously.

When Utter returns, he finds a parody. She walks around wearing a brooch of carrots and leading her goat, trying to be a flower child. This look could be beatnik at nineteen, even now at fifty-three; but she's become arrogant, and that makes the gypsy schtick seem tired. On top of that though, she actually is selling her work, and so is Maurice, and Utter is miles behind.

✳

Can I say you're making me want to throw up?

'I mek myself warnt to throw up. And this moment is where everyfing go wrong. You can pinpoint that moment, you know?'

Yeah. Though sometimes it comes more than once.

14

I started meeting him in London every Friday night. Until in a half-deserted Dalston saloon, he said, 'See that woman across the bar?' I looked. 'Which of us d'you think can get her?'

'What?'

He glanced at this middle-aged woman and smiled. She half-smiled back, showing ropey teeth, and touched her hair. I looked at her and held her gaze. I think we both must've thought, what is going on? Adam got up, moved to our side of the bar, put his hands on it and considered her as if he was already making love to her. I got my bag and left.

It was November. We walked to the flat in silence and upstairs, he pushed me against the freezing wall, ripped down my jeans and was inside me in seconds. Adam was careful on sexual health, and we'd more or less given up using protection for any other reason; I'd had so much wrong after Nick I'd been told I had little chance of getting pregnant naturally. When he'd come, he went to the kitchen and opened a beer, called someone from the phone on the wall and talked like I wasn't there. At dawn, trying to hang on to something in my isolated world and be fun, I went to the Indian shop and got him a Freddo. When I came back, he was awake but not up.

'You're a disappointment, Glyn. You don't really have talent but you don't even try. You'll always be a failure.'

His chest was very white, I noticed. And hairless, like a chihuahua.

'And you've got boring, stuck up in that weird dumb-fuck land. Without your gang, what are you? Yet for some confusing reason, because you write adult fiction, allegedly, and I write kids' books, you think you're great.'

I think I'm..? There comes a point where you're just not shocked anymore, or even really that surprised. You're only surprised at yourself.

As I closed the door behind me for the last time, I heard him on the phone again, then I heard him sneeze. 'Yeah bro, I can come over now.' He laughed. 'She's just leaving...'

A week later, I had flu. Ten days later – just after I'd applied for a student hardship grant because the tenants' rent wasn't even covering the flat's mortgage and though I still worked remotely I was living on baked beans – I realised I was pregnant. A little baby that had magicked itself up against the odds and come to keep me company. That I couldn't afford to have.

∗

This is all a bit gloomy, innit?

∗

1923. Suzanne is fifty-eight and Utter's thirty-seven. She's ageing badly now, and a shrew because she thinks he's looking at other women, and he is. He gives up painting because he can make more money agenting Suzanne and Maurice, and it makes him sick that he's better at business than art.

Abandoning the youthful act, Suzanne works on a self-portrait no other woman on earth would paint, even now; bare, drooping breasts, hollow cheeks, a mouth so drawn she's probably got badly made false teeth in there. She'll paint another at sixty-seven, more decrepit, her neck gone like it does at that age, breasts exposed, face serious, a workhorse still pushing boundaries, using the body that for years now is all that's paid for her to live. This is who I am, André, she's saying. You knew it would come to this. Utter glances at the work, then sells it.

∗

When I finally got through to Adam, he said, 'Your timing, Glyn. It's shit.'

202

The storage heaters still wouldn't work properly. One morning, I got up to feed the cats and the windows were blurry. When I put my finger against the pane, it stuck, then the sheet of ice inside started to melt.

✳

In a Georgian house by Greenwich Park, I'm forking up expensive Country Hunter Chicken & Goose Dinner for Keats and Lorca. Keats is ancient and I need to watch his food intake like a hawk. But I can't find him. And then he strolls in from the garden, a dying bird in his mouth. 'Keats! You bastard!'

He looks at me, not bothered. Get down on my knees and try to prise open the cat's jaws. A low growl in the back of the throat. A sound from the bird. 'Fucking fucker!'

The sparrow is helpless. Innocent. The cat bites down, staring me out. A wing moves and stops.

'I hate you!' Swipe at him but he's gone, victorious, guzzling hot blood.

I'm crying. Wipe my nose on my sleeve.

Stand up, and notice for the first time there's a camera on the workbench computer trained on me. Gaze at it in horror. Are the owners recording me? Are they watching me now?

✳

André cheats, then cheats again.

What keeps her going? 'When I paint,' she said, 'I feel I'm worth something.' Sounds like Tracey Emin. The few other female artists, privileged like Mary Cassat, painted pretty women dressed with taste. Male artists who looked at women sanctified them or got aroused and painted them for other men. But the body's owner just scrutinises her arms, sees blood on her thighs and wipes it off. Not posed, Valadon's women are turned awkwardly or looking for something. Or they glare at you. And because she had no training, she couldn't see how much she shocked.

✳

Maurice, completely mad, marries a widow who takes control of his money. Seventy now, her value falling, Suzanne has nothing, flogging paintings to buy steak if Utter drops by. But at forty-nine, having affairs with thirty-year-olds, he rarely comes. The fiery girl who danced, sang, painted with him. This person? It actually is as if he's come to see his mother.

✳

I moved into the Hackney spare room of a friend's rocker friend over Christmas so I could do holiday cover on a TV mag, the cats parked with another mate.

Drenched with hormones, I was superhuman. I stepped into the road outside the office one lunchtime and felt I could stop a juggernaut with my hand. Away from the loneliness of the boathouse, my spirits treacherously rose. The slender gap in me that thought about having children opened up. Little fingers, forming... Did it have ears yet? Could it hear me? There was nothing wrong with this baby, no tablets to damage it like last time. I thought about giving up the degree, moving home to look for work, if I could. But in the middle of a recession, magazines were crashing like cars. I could lose the flat. Could I get a council flat? Which would be on an estate in Dalston or Clapton's Murder Mile, and what would a tiny baby's life be like there?

Still, filled with unexpected emotions, I tried to work out how to keep it. Sat in this room at night, the friend's friend's weirdo flatmate doing something weird in his room, scribbling figures on an envelope – mortgage, food, gas, electric, nursery for a baby at a month, weeks, days old. Could I find full-time or freelance gigs, as I got more and more pregnant? And I was in this skint position because I'd *stupidly* tried to do something arty.

Two nights before the abortion, someone thumped on the door.

'Adam?'

'Can I come in?' He pushed past me, looking round the room, which was a toilet, rubberwear fetish posters all over the walls that I didn't want the baby to see. He sat on a box of books. 'I'm coming to the clinic with you.'

'No you're not.'

'Yeah, been talking to my female friends. They say I need closure on this.'

'You?'

He nodded. 'Don't want to be upset by it in the future. Plus I need to make sure you do it.' He put his hands behind his head, leaned back. 'You still want me, don't you? Even now.'

Despite my preternatural new powers, I struggled to drag him to his feet. He guffawed.

'Get out. Get... OUT!'

I manhandled him through the door, panting, and heard the echo of his laugh as he clattered down the stone stairwell.

I couldn't keep a link to this person in my life. He'd have to have access, see the child, his parents would pay for legal help to make sure of it.

I don't really want to say much about the operation, three days before Christmas Eve. The TV in the recovery room, with a chatty breakfast show about festive snacks when we were all groggy with anaesthetic and numb disillusion. At least Adam wasn't there. A doctor, signing a slip saying they'd 'regulated my periods', said, 'You can't have another abortion, it'll leave you prone to miscarriage.' Oh, okay. It's been fun but I'll stop.

Charlie came to get me in a cab, took me back to hers, put me to bed and let me sob into my lentil soup. I tried to ring Adam to scream that it was done, but it turned out he was getting closure at a party.

✳

Suzanne remained in her studio because when she worked, her spirit soared out of her creaking body. Calm and alone, she grew happier. She painted a vase and on its side, the words

'Joie de vivre'. She used gorgeous colours, ochre, gold, russet brown, deep blue and magenta. Still lifes of wine bottles, apples, dead pheasants, blossoms you can smell the scent of, jasmine and rose. Everything blazing, vivid and sweet.

She was at her easel one April morning when she had a stroke. She was seventy-three, but part of her actually was still the funny, raucous imp who'd swung from railings. Look at her, painting then glancing round at you. She died on her way to the hospital. Seeing beauty, beauty, beauty.

✳

'And so you don't have ze baby?'

No, as it happens. I didn't wind up with a baby at the end of it. I wound up standing outside Victoria station, smoking and waiting for my sister because, get this, ever hopeful we were catching a train to my Dad and Deirdre's for Christmas. Except one of us slipped up, he found out what had happened and as Deirdre ran from the room, face contorted, gagging, he suggested that if I couldn't control my sexual urges, I should get sterilised. It was a lovely relaxing break.

✳

Me and Maggie got back to London and before she caught the train to Scotland, we went to see *Cinema Paradiso*. There's that long, long scene at the end where a million couples run into each other's arms, full of happiness and fulfilment, and she knew I was crying in the dark and put her hand on mine, and after the lights came up we sat motionless, raccoon faces wet with mascara. Outside, wiping her cheek, she said, 'I'm going to Adam's. I'm just going to kill him.'

And I said oh no, no need for that, I'm okay really. I walked her to King's Cross and we said goodbye, and I watched her trundle with her bag down the platform, turning every few minutes to wave, and squinted like I always do after everyone else had gone and the train had pulled out and I couldn't see any more sign of it, not even the tiniest speck.

206

Outside, I got the bus to Dalston. I knocked on Adam's door and was pleased when I heard his feet strolling along the hall. He opened up and I kangaroo punched him in the face. He put his hands to his nose. 'Jesus Christ! You fucking mad-woman. Get away from me.'

His nose was bleeding. I turned round and walked down the steps. I'd always hated those ugly steps.

'I'm calling the police!' What an infantile voice Adam had, especially if shrieking. And crying. 'Can you hear me? You fucking psycho bitch!'

At Beigel Bake, I stopped to get myself something. Then I headed to my crappy lodgings, went upstairs and started to pack.

✳

The boathouse was bitter. I unlocked the door, hauled in the cat baskets. Sat and fiddled with the storage heaters. I pressed 'Boost', which had never worked, and something came on. They couldn't be charging?

I filled the cat tray with clean litter and headed up to campus to get any paperwork. In my cubbyhole was a letter from the university; I'd been awarded the hardship grant. I stood there re-reading it. Then I cycled to Tesco and got some okay coffee and two Twixes and some fancy cat food.

When I got in it was dark. And bloody warm in there. Up on the mezzanine, Fin was sprawled on the bed. I stroked Bessie and she purred like a drill.

I snapped on my desk lamp, lit a Silk Cut, scribbled a quick card to Maggie, rolled a sheet of paper into the typewriter and concentrated like I'd never concentrated before. Let the thing I've done not be for nothing.

✳

I heard stories about Adam messing with advanced drugs, three-somes with whores and other men, surprise. At the end of these calls, I'd pull on a coat and walk the lanes, breathing clean air.

Last I heard, he was living in Manhattan with a trans

prostitute. When someone said she'd tried to put his eye out with a fork, it was quite a while before I stopped laughing.

✳

'I admire you.'

Oh? Well, I admire you, now I understand the big picture. There's a quote of yours, what was it? *I had great masters. I took the best of their examples and I found myself, I made myself, and I said what I had to say.* You were most amazing of all toward the end. When at one point you'd done a good impression of a desperate, idiotic douche.

'Ditto, chérie.'

I know. I do know.

'Well, finally I could look at what I was, not how I wished I could be. It's not easy but it's better. Can you do that now?'

Look at what I am? I think so.

'Really?'

I said I think so! Jesus.

✳

Turn off the computer. I'd stopped the running but I think I should start again. I felt better when I did it. Find my trainers and walk to the park.

There's no one here, because it's a weekday. Stand and look at the trees.

'It's beautiful. You see that?'

Yes.

'Good, if I could see it, you can. It's a matter of letting yourself.'

You've stopped that funny voice. Or I have. I'd seen something needy and posturing of myself in you and I ridiculed it. Unfair to us both.

Cough and launch myself off. Huff and puff. A squirrel. A jay. Parakeets, wheeling in the air and squeaking that delirious shriek.

I'd thought I might cry again, but there truly is still beauty.

15

X marks the spot

Fly the Jolly Roger from your own Black Pearl

I got caught on a video at Keats's house. Terry arrived the next day announced by a very quiet knock, always a bad sign. He's a little guy but he supports Millwall and he used to be a bouncer.

'Did you hit Keats? They've got a surveillance camera inside, I meant to tell you but I shouldn't need to.'

'I didn't touch him, Terry. I tried to open his jaw, he was killing a bird.'

'Are you insane, it's what they *do*. Just watch your step. Watch it.'

How many other cameras exist? Once he's gone, I have to sit down. I've been playing Cat-Feeder Russian Roulette, because I've been nosier than you think. And sometimes people wanted me to see things, I know they did. Like the morning I arrived at Antony and Cleo's and, posturing in the post rack by the door – open, unfolded – was Otter's pension statement. Why would you leave something so important there? Do they think I can't read? The amount she'd 'accrued' blew my mind. They already didn't have to worry about the future; if they're so stressed, why didn't Ratty and Otter rent out their enormous house and take off round the world? They might stumble on jobs they'd actually enjoy.

I've looked at other things. Seen builders' estimates for work done in some of the biggest Georgian houses on Crooms Hill or Eliot Vale and been horrified at the inflated prices these people get charged by feral oiks like my dad's family. I've sat on the toilet – one ultra-chic house in Lee has a heated seat, you could sit there a long time – going through clothing catalogues featuring cashmere sweatshirts and funky silk skirts so upmarket they don't have prices. I've tried exotic beauty products and read Valentines, though not diaries because I couldn't find any. I don't want to know about sex toys. Napoleon was playing with a pair of crotchless knickers one afternoon and I left him to it – he was ruining them but what do you do, put them in a drawer? What if they'd been worn? The odd thing is, I've only gone round looking in quite posh houses. Partly because, yes, I wonder how they got what they have, though I can't trace it to anything other than background and connections. But also, some of the richer people (though not all) are not very nice in their notes, and I need to get even. The shabbier the house, on the whole the nicer the note and the more homemade chocolate fridge cake they leave for me.

*

Terry turns up with this week's roster, flipping through the cards like a poker hand and giving a quick spiel with each one like he does. 'Houdini, new hiding place next door's bathroom so don't panic if he ain't there. Shadow, Belmont Hill. They leave him in the conservatory so you need to let him out the garden, then get him back in. Take their wheelie bins to the end of the drive Thursday, bring 'em back up Friday.'

'What if he won't come in?'

'Don't let him out if there's no time. They won't know. But he's stuck in there all day.'

I'll let him out.

'Ronnie, Reggie and Jack the Cat in Deptford Market. Looks like a shop. Art installation thing inside, weird stuff if you ask me. Then Mimi and Ferragamo at the Admiral's house. Finally James Bond in New Cross, take the narrow road on the right just behind the fire station and there's a gated estate. Camera in the hallway. I've put it on the card.' Look at the card. 'CAMERA IN HALLWAY!!!'

210

Smile at him. 'Thanks, mate.'

'And alarm in the meter cupboard on your left as you go in.'

Fucking hell. This should be a laugh.

✳

I emerged from college with an MA and a determination that next year would be better, though I'd enjoyed the last months and made lasting friendships. What I'd done that Christmas had been right, I knew it; I put it away in a box in my mind where I'd go to see it often, but gradually less. And I felt renewed without Adam. I had to come at life differently.

Finally the cats and I were all home. I found that stint on the *Post* news magazine, which turned into a contract. I was back in the world I knew, and with income. I stayed up every night, again, trying to write fiction. Then Paul – still in touch, that's how decent he is – told me *Time Out* was running a short story competition. I came up with an idea and posted what I'd written on the way to work.

I won the competition. That's London for you. It is my drug.

✳

At the Admiral's house, feed Mimi. She and Ferragamo were rescued from starvation by the Admiral and his child bride in the Italian village where they have a second home. Mimi is a boisterous tabby, and her food is laid out on the big kitchen table that she likes to scatter with Felix meaty chunks. It looks like something from *La Grande Bouffe*. Ferragamo is shy and inhabits the upper regions of a house so tall you need crampons and an oxygen tank to reach the summit. Clawing my way to the highest bathroom, where he likes to eat, curse as I realise he's out of Science Diet, which means going back again. While I brace myself, stare out of a window. It's actually more like being in the crow's nest of a ship. This must be why the Admiral bought it, when he could run up the stairs and

211

relive his Navy days, not arthritically crawl halfway as he does now. Look over the rooftops of Maritime Greenwich to the turbulent waves of the Thames, which lead to the open sea.

'Behind you, mamacita! Take him down, or shall I? Oh, so tragic, sir, you fell into the ocean. And you don't seem to swim too good.'

Let's say Mary Read, the pirate who died of pregnancy complications in Port Royal, Jamaica, didn't look exactly like the romantically androgynous but potentially lethal version of her above. And let's say Anne Bonny also wasn't the way fantasy games and obscure films portray her: a redheaded Demelza Poldark with a bushwhacker hat. Let's say it, even though there's a fighting chance they weren't far removed from this (they were good-looking. There's evidence). What you can't deny is that they battled side by side, and back to back, more brilliantly and courageously than most male pirates, an 18th-century Thelma and Louise.

Not an easy life on a criminal ship. Not actually that much rum. Nothing to eat but turtle. The girls got so little food it's likely their periods were few and far between, and they were muscled and wiry as boys from shinning up the rigging and mortal combat. Bonny couldn't keep her hands off men, but the theory is that the women were so deeply attached, they'd have been happy together. I see that. Apart from the captain, Bonny's lover, they were the most magnetic people on board. Keira Knightley as the Pirate King, running the ship with Penelope Cruz as Blackbeard's daughter Angelica? Not much, because those two had clashing egos. Frankly, the key thing Read and Bonny and the *Pirates of the Caribbean* movies have in common is the Caribbean.

Which must be one of piracy's biggest draws. Say you're Mary, born in 1685 in picturesque but damp Devon. Wouldn't you want to wind up in a place with azure sky, hot sand between your toes? If you were poor but wanted this, plus autonomy in a world where women didn't get it, you'd have to become that aberrant thing, a female buccaneer.

According to Captain Charles Johnson and Daniel Defoe's *A General History of the Robberies and Murders of the Most Notorious Pyrates*, 1724, which could be accurate or not, Mary's mother was married to a sailor, and they had a baby son, Mark. The sailor deserted his family and she had an affair, getting pregnant with Mary; just months into this, Mark became ill and died. The sailor's mother had been donating occasional cash to keep the little boy, so his death was concealed and the new baby dressed in her half-brother's clothes and named Mark. For thirteen years she grew up as a boy. Then the grandmother died.

'I was tall, handsome, quite liked fighting. I stayed Mark.'

Mark got a job as a footboy for a wealthy French widow – his mother's idea, quite clever. 'In London. But she started to really like me. Flirting. Appalling.'

He left and signed up as a powder monkey, stoking the cannons on a man-o-war, then jumped ship and went to Flanders. There was a war on. Five foot eight and lanky now, he joined a regiment of foot soldiers as a cadet.

One description of Read's life at this time relates: 'Though in every action she conducted herself with the greatest bravery, yet she could not obtain a commission,' that is, become an officer, 'as they were in general bought and sold.'

A stream of tobacco shoots across the room. Ugh, clean that up. I mean... It's okay, I'll clean it. Not that it's even there. 'Every bloke who moves up the ranks is loaded, officer jobs purchased for them even if they're useless. I wanted to wring their scrawny necks.'

'You'd do it too, darlin'. Ya have the temper on you still. Have a lovely way with that temper, the flash of the eyes.' So now I've got two lady pirates in my room. Anne Bonny might've died in Carolina (possibly. No one's sure) and grown up in the Deep South but there's still a whisper of her mother's County Cork in her voice. She takes Read's cleft chin in silver-ringed fingers. Can we concentrate, girls?

So teenage Mark Read leaves the infantry and joins the cavalry, where he distinguishes himself in battle. A lad with no beard yet, but clever and fearless.

'And then I fell in love. Couldn't stop myself. You should've seen the man in question.'

Mark/Mary was paired with a Flemish soldier. They bonded, as fighters do, guarding each other, galloping beside each other. Sharing a tent.

'What passed for a tent. And I just wanted to touch him, it really shocked me. He'd strip off for battle, and...' Right. 'I needed something more. Despite my conditioning.'

Very tricky when you're practically living with him.

'I had a little shtick I went through when I dressed and whatever, concealing myself. But one night I let my shirt slip. He could've turned me in. But he was, ah, pleasantly surprised.'

I should think he was.

'And so was I. And it was pretty good, except he thought

we could work together every day and I could be his mistress all evening. But I'm used to the military and taking the initiative. I said he'd have to court me, then try to get me to marry him.' She inclines her head. 'Which he did.'

So you both came out?

'We said hello everyone he's a man, I'm a lady, we're getting married and buying ourselves out of the service. A couple of the officers needed smelling salts.'

The cavalry unit were bowled over. They chipped in to buy Mary her first-ever women's clothes, which she found preposterous in terms of getting them on, 'But no big deal if you've worn armour.' The wedding itself had a full and rowdy turnout, and after that the pair packed up and, with the wedding present money, opened a pub, the Three Horseshoes, near the picturesque fortified Dutch city of Breda.

All set.

'I thought so.'

✳

Me too. Was loving my life. The *Post* was quite exciting and almost Hildy Johnson, even though it was right-wing and I was just a sub. I had some stories published in fiction collections. My days were wonderful.

One evening, my phone rang. A deep, humorous voice. 'It's Benjamin, don't know if you remember. We met briefly at *City Limits* when Toni was doing that receptionist stint...'

Toni, my ditzy Brooklyn pal. Okay, yes, I know you.

'She told me you were back in London, gave me your number. Would you like to meet for coffee? I'd love to hear about the MA course. I'm deeply impressed.'

I didn't think I was that interested, but a few days later I pedal to Old Compton Street and there he is. A tall, dark and quirkily handsome Jeff Goldblum type, a struggling academic journo with a PhD from Oxford, two years' teaching experience at the Sorbonne and a Russian violinist mother. He grins sheepishly and very sexily, which I hadn't registered before because I'd been obsessed with Nick, and asks about the course even though that's just a line. He seems impressed I'm academic (I'm the furthest from academic), when clearly I look, in my strappy elastane bodysuit, leggings and yellow nail varnish, so very un-academic, so I'm sure for him it's a nice surprise, like when your fellow cavalryman turns out to be a girl or you find the Jack Nicholson redneck in *Five Easy Pieces* is a cultured prodigy. Though I'm really Nicholson's trashy girlfriend Rayette.

The following week he invites me to a movie, since he's keen to be a film reviewer, and I have to tell the *Post* team at 6.30pm, which is mid-afternoon on a news magazine, that I'd like to do it if I can and they rally round, when we're going to press in an hour, and just yell at me, 'Go, get out, have fun!'

We continue like this for weeks, meeting, talking, and like Mary Read my frustration becomes intense, unbearable. And then one night it all suddenly happens. I'm in heaven. Call Maggie. 'Brilliant news,' she says. 'So you're a shiksa?'

I am! Later, look the word up, thinking how glamorous – the forbidden seductress – it sounds. Used by the Jewish community for a gentile girl or woman. From the word 'sheqes', 'a detested thing'. Well, let's forget about that.

We spend Christmas together, though he arrives at about 11pm on Christmas Eve, but that's fine, I only got back from work two hours ago. I've bought him a soft black roll-neck. He's got me two Christmas crackers. I don't care (well, I care a bit, but this is not his festival). Next day, when I'm drunk and trying to get a chicken into the oven I have never used, he calls his mother to ask how you roast a chicken, and she's beyond horrified. He hands me the receiver. A frail, heavily accented voice. 'So, Benjamin tells me you can't cook?' As I start to reply, one internal wall of the oven falls in with a clang and I have to stuff my fist in my mouth.

216

✳

'I have the face of a clown.'

'Of course you don't have the face of a clown, you clown.'

'Oh,' in Joe Pesci voice, 'you think I'm fonnee? Dat I'm here to amuse you?' In Pesci mode, walking round me in my tiny bedroom, hitting his chest. 'I'm a clown, I'm funny how? Whereas you – you are beeyotiful woman.' He drops the act. 'You are. Beautiful.'

'You're beautiful. Can't you see that?' Stroke his angular, gorgeous face.

'You're being kind.' He clasps my hand. 'I'm just clever. Or I thought I was.'

Sigh, roll my eyes.

'You're too good for me. Prize-winning writer, yadda yadda.'

'What yadda? One thing.'

'But a big thing. Listen, can I ask you something? Can I read you a piece I wrote on spec for *Film International*?'

'I'd be pleased to hear it.'

So we lie on the bed and he reads this piece. It's over my head but it sounds good. 'Is it okay?'

'You're a fabulous writer. Send it off.'

So he does.

He is wonderful to be with. He is ridiculously entertaining. He wants to make movies. He takes me to Hampstead for lunch with his parents, his irascible retired solicitor father, his gentle, ferociously bright mother. A brave woman who at eighteen played a recital in wartime London and when the sirens struck up, continued to play, so that audience members who'd been leaving to find air-raid shelters slowly returned and together they defied the bombs.

It occurs to me that if we had children, they would not be Jewish, and this is important to her. But his happiness is more important. When we leave it's snowing. She finds a hat, a soft

217

fur Cossack hat of her own, and puts it on me, and smilingly cups my face in her palms. 'My leetle Ninotchka.'

✳

Mary's husband caught a fever and died, an illness we'd now cure in days with antibiotics. Distraught, she tried to make the inn work on her own but her heart wasn't in it and the business collapsed.

What do you do? You do what you know. She dragged out her old male clothes, headed to the coast and tried something new, applying to join a Dutch merchant ship trading overseas. It was intolerably boring. And then, en route to the West Indies, the plodding windjammer was trounced by English pirates lead by ultimate professional Charles Vane. Vane was wily, successful and cruel. On the other hand, this was at least interesting. As the only Englishman on the Dutch ship, Mark Read was given the option of joining the pirate crew. He said yes.

Pirate ship existence was dirtier than on a Dutch trader. Cramped, damp quarters, filth where there'd been some attempt at hygiene, and death always waiting. Now thirty-two, Read was binding her breasts, making sure no one saw blood if she had a period, training regularly to match any man. A year later, King George offered pirates an amnesty. Read took it. And was bored.

'But then I was offered a job on a privateer, where the government encourages ships to attack foreign vessels and bring them back as prizes. Just lawfully attack. Which did sound like fun.'

You're a maniac, you know that?

Anne intervenes. 'For the most part we're actually professionals. It's good to be good at something, and we're good with a cutlass and a pistol. Protect your weapon at all times, and your strong right arm.'

I'm left-handed.

Mark says, 'So am I.

218

16

The prize for winning the *Time Out* competition was a computer, a little Apple Mac LC, Elsie; my Olympia glowered. I said, 'I'll never use this', and Benjamin said, 'You will, you'll forget the typewriter'. And he was right. It was fabulous to just delete a mistake and not have to cover everything including your entire body in Tipp-Ex.

I was still trying to scribble stories, but every time I got home, about 9pm, and switched on the computer, the phone would ring as if a signal had spun through the wiring. Ben was writing more and more successfully.

'Can I read you something, sweetheart?'

'Well, I was working, you know, trying to, but...'

'Just quickly.'

So I'd light a cigarette and listen. And after that we'd talk. And then I'd realise it was midnight, and I hadn't eaten anything, and there were six hours till getting-up time.

He was going to film previews most evenings. Often I went too, just to be with him. We'd sit side by side for two hours, then go to some Soho bar with the other movie critics, and once they'd established I knew nothing about the director I would be ignored. As the talk of long shots, tracking shots, French avant-garde swirled in the air, I would be so, so bored.

My precious after-work writing time, dematerialising.

Had I learned nothing? Passion had undone me again. Must be the way I did love, I never became a zen master. I'd start off with a sabre and when my opponent asked for it, I'd hand it over. That's just pathetic.

Meanwhile, I'd created a monster. I'd told Ben how great he was, and his confidence grew as mine was fading. It's like

A Star is Born. A movie you hate, Ben. Tell you something? I even like the Streisand version.

✳

'Ahoy there. We mean to come aboard. Have you any objection?'

Mark can't believe his eyes. It's the Golden Age of Piracy, they're in the Bahamas just off Nassau, and there's a huge ship. Spyglass? The *Revenge*. Oops, it's very close all of a sudden. And the man hailing them from the deck is... ridiculous. John Rackham, alias Captain Calico Jack, got his fame by leading a mutiny against Charles Vane. And he got his name because he dresses in eye-wateringly bright, though faded by sun, Indian calico. We're talking chintzy Captain Jack Sparrow and then some. From the bridge of the *Revenge*, Rackham waves a grubby, emerald-coated arm. 'I'd put those cannons away if I were you.'

Mark glances toward his own captain and in the second he does, five cannons on the *Revenge* unloose shots and the square-rigged brigantine unfurls a skull and crossed swords (a design invented by Calico Jack, in fact). Its crew swarms over the rails and everyone on the frigate is either dead or captive. Apart from Mark, who stands panting, cutlass in hand and two casualties at his feet.

'You were all very surprised how we did that, weren't you?' Calico Jack sighs as he picks his way down the deck. 'And you, young man...' He arches an eyebrow at Mark, 'can come with us. Yes? All sorts of adventures planned and all –' he widens his eyes 'amid these lovely warm seas.'

✳

Ben was beginning to establish himself. He had a regular column in a respected cinema monthly. He got his first picture byline, and looked like Vronsky.

On one rare weekend when he wasn't writing, we took the train to Sussex to see Dad and Deirdre, who still lived there

220

then. I suppose if you only have one parent, you keep hoping. Our train was delayed. Dad met us at the station and we drove to their semi in silence. Deirdre was washing up. 'We have our dinner at twelve o'clock, so we've finished. Yours is there.'

I handed her the flowers I'd got her, past the congealed food on the table, which I sat down with Ben to eat. Watching us coolly, she said, 'Seen 'is 'air, Charlie?'

I looked at Ben's black corkscrew curls. 'Looks like a mad professor, dunt'ee?' She cackled, then leaned forward and spoke as if he were deficient. 'Your parents, are they...' She searched her mind. 'Strict Jews?'

'Orthodox?' Head on one side, brow raised, gentle and polite.

'No, are they real Jews? Do they go to church? What's it called, Charlie?' Too excited to wait for 'synagogue', wouldn't know 'mensch' if it said shalom. 'Is your mum's head shaved?'

She patted her perm and chuckled. Dad folded his arms, smiling tenderly. If I think back, Deirdre's laugh in those days was very like a parrot's. Pieces of eight.

No point apologising. The fact that this was my family was punishment enough.

✳

Sex had a major role. It was a significant part of Ben's being. I watched him interview a soignée French film-maker at the French Institute, in French. I mean I watched, I didn't understand, but I smiled and laughed along with everyone else as if I did. Frowning, nodding, oh, I wasn't aware, how interesting. When we left and waited for the bus I hadn't much to say, not knowing what had been said, but I tried not to be Rayette and asked in a throwaway way, 'Did that go as you expected?'

He said, 'What did you think of the "*Je T'aime*" comments?'

221

I waited. I knew the song but was that what he meant? I began to feel jealous.

He drew me down an alley. 'That line of Gainsbourg's, remember? She used the song in the love scene, where the camera lingers on the penetration. "Je vais and je viens, entre tes reins..." I come between your loins.' He smoothed hair from my lips. 'Your kidneys is what it means.'

'Maybe my kidneys are happy together and don't want you coming between them.'

He lowered his mouth.

✳

A weekend in Paris. Except obviously I didn't have him to myself even then, he was looking up friends from Sorbonne days. Most were French, and I sat in the room as conversation floated around me, *une* soul *perdue*. Later in a bar, Benjamin seemed incandescent as he chatted with one man, Jérôme. I drifted on the fringes like a dying balloon.

'What about her? She's not bad and she's on her own.'

I turned. Two English chaps on holiday, clearly thinking everyone in this bar was French because no one was speaking English. They'd seen me and thought...

'Bonswar,' one said to me. I sniffed. 'It's okay, I'm from Hackney.'

They laughed, and I said, 'I'm with him,' and turned away, even though I felt happy that I looked good enough to be French.

When we left and walked through the narrow streets to our room I said, 'Can we spend tomorrow just by ourselves?'

'I really want to see Jérôme then. We're leaving next day.' I know. 'And he... All right, he was the first man I kissed.'

The rest of the walk was very quiet as my brain reeled. I thought, but it's okay, that's history now. Back home, I ran it by Toni. 'Oh gard, why are English men all fags?'

That made it funny. 'He's not a fag. He's just sexy.'

222

'Too sexy for his shirt.' She snapped her fingers and danced on the pavement, singing. 'I'm too sexy for Milan, New York and Japan...'

'Too sexy for Finsbury Park, anyway.'

✳

I realised I was speaking in a stilted way, trying to sound middle class, or at least cultured. I felt I was walking through a minefield, carefully adding 'h's, or 't's where before there'd been glottal stops. I didn't know how so many words should be said, and if I didn't know how to say something coming up in a sentence, I rephrased my sentence. I still made mistakes. I thought Imogen was pronounced 'Imoggen'. I said 'Go-eth' when I should've said Goethe. I'd probably have said 'Ver-sayse' if I was interested in fashion.

Toni once told me the reason she got married the first time was, 'I could fart in front of him.' I said, 'Gross.' But now I couldn't even talk without shame.

At a party I wandered the floors, searching for Ben. Then I saw him. An arm against the wall in a predatory way, this posh girl screenwriter from the French Institute leaning back on the wall, posing up at him. Both smoking. Ben didn't smoke.

I walked across. 'Hi. It's Imoggen, isn't it? Here's an ashtray, or *cendrier*. You're dropping ash on the carpet.'

17

'And who should I meet aboard the *Revenge* but Calico Jack's second in command. Who had the swagger of a long-haired youth.'

'And I saw a handsome beast.'

Two female pirates on the same ship. And though Bonny was having a covert affair with Jack, she also wanted Mark.

Anne was still a teenager. Born in County Cork in 1700, result of a scandalous affair between servant Mary Brennan and her married employer, lawyer William Cormac. Cormac moved the small family to London, dressed the girl as a boy and called her Andrew (Andrew?), saying she was his apprentice, training as a lawyer's clerk. But his wife was on his trail, so he decamped with the child and her mother to Charleston, South Carolina, and Brennan died almost immediately of typhoid. The twelve-year-old girl was red-haired and striking, but she had a terrifying temper; when a boy assaulted her, she beat him so badly 'he lay ill of it a considerable time'.

Anne married small-time pirate James Bonny and, appalled, Cormac disowned her. When she was fourteen, she and Bonny found their way to Nassau, a criminal sanctuary nicknamed the Republic of Pirates. But James accepted clemency, becoming an informer, and Anne disliked that. She met Calico Jack in a tavern and left James for him, becoming a full-blooded pirate disguised from all but the captain.

And it's delightful until Mister Read appears. Anne is insatiably attracted. She works alongside him, she banters disarmingly, and when she can't stand it any longer she follows him into a storeroom, locks the door and in time-honoured fashion tears open her shirt. 'I'm a woman, Mister Read.'

Well, have I got news for you. As I understand it, they became lovers on the spot.

✳

Jack wasn't stupid. He thought there was something going on. His bird and that bastard from the privateer. Ungrateful bugger! So, as in a Brian Rix farce, one day he breaks in on them, in bed in his private quarters.

'And the only way to quiet him down was suggesting a *ménage à trois*. Which I think we all enjoyed. Did you enjoy it, Mary?'

'Oh yes.'

The three of them, a triumvirate of strength and cunning, lead their crew and take on vessel after vessel, capturing ships, pillaging and looting, feared across the high seas. Anne becomes pregnant, which is a bit revealing as men generally can't do it; after she's had the baby and left it with a family in Cuba, she returns to the ship where, everything out in the open, Jack marries her, probably officiating at his own wedding. 'Do you, Jack Rackham..? 'I do, sir.'

But Jack grows reckless. He begins to take risks, heading into popular sea lanes stuffed with merchant ships full of plunder instead of attacking when they're off-course and vulnerable.

✳

A brief trip to Corsica. Stroking my hair, Ben said, 'I want to write fiction, I always have. Can you talk me through it, show me how to get started?'

225

And I realised I'd forgotten.

Swimming together, he said, 'If we had children, they'd be stupid, because you don't read a newspaper, do you?' We'd never talked about kids, only ever hinted. On the beach he grinned, towelling his back. 'Had a wank in the sea. All the little sperm, swimming away.'

Not put in Dopey, then.

I was too timid to go down to the breakfast room in the morning and face other guests. My confidence, in ribbons, fluttered in the breeze.

We got chatting to another English couple. Or Benjamin did, I was more or less mute. When they heard we were journalists and I was looking for work, the woman suggested Ben give me a review for the mag he now edited.

He sipped his drink. 'I don't trust her judgement.'

I don't trust her judgement?

The Hackney irregulars, who'd met Benjamin only once or twice, had stopped inviting us to things. They tried but they didn't like him. 'Plus he's grown a goatee.'

Say I realise that. He looks good.

'When it comes to trust,' said my pal, who I'd told about Corsica, 'never trust a guy with a goatee.'

✳

October 1720. By now, the *Revenge* was spoken of not just throughout the Caribbean, but famed in the North American colonies, wanted by bounty hunters as far as England. When he saw a well-rigged ship, Rackham would approach at speed and slurringly invite his victims over: 'We are Englishmen! Come on board and have some punch.' When like fools they came, Anne and Mary, his attack-dogs, would lead the slaughter, dragging back cargo and treasure worth thousands.

The reward money for the trio had reached the level of a lottery rollover, and pirate hunter Captain Jonathan Barnet, famously merciless, eventually tracked them down, a large furled vessel lying at anchor in a mosquito-infested cove off Jamaica's Negril Bay. He'd brought a second ship lead by a Captain Bonnevie as backup. Out of sight, Barnet and Bonnevie waited for dark.

On board the *Revenge*, Anne and Mary paced the floor in Rackham's cabin, trying to talk sense to him. Off his head on stolen booze, he'd decided to have a party. Rolling their eyes, Anne and Mary began the night watch, alone.

At about ten o'clock, Barnet hoisted his anchor and closed the gap between the ships. He braced his men, then bellowed: 'Captain of the *Revenge*!'

Anne went to fetch Rackham, who appeared at the helm, swaying, and saw the small fleet across the water. 'Jack Rackham, from Cuba,' he announced, continuing proudly that he would give no quarter. He turned to his paralytic crew, 'Ready the guns!'

Too late. Barnet fired cannons, ripping the ship's gun-holding broadside. In a drunken panic Rackham ordered his men to go below. They fell over themselves into the hold and locked the trapdoor, leaving Anne and Mary to defend them.

✳

So it's not quite as humorous as we'd like now. Mary booted the locked door. 'If there's a man among ye, ye'll come up and fight!' Nothing; actually, several called out for surrender. Disgusted, she fired down into the hold, killing one of her own crew. 'You spineless morons!'

Mary and Anne, together, with just a handful of their companions having the guts to emerge and support them, battle the intruders. 'Watch on the left!'

'Your own right!'

'By the mast!'

'Fuck, fuck...'

They were called by those who saw the fight 'a brace of hellcats'. One of them twenty, one thirty-five, swinging here,

227

slashing there. Jack, do something? He declines.

I can watch it from so far away, looking back down the corridor of years and seeing it play out in slow motion. Jim Morrison sings 'The End' as bloody streaks appear on the women's arms and faces. 'This is the end, beautiful friend... This is the end, my only friend, the end.'

It takes an hour, but the battle was over before it began. 'It's finished, mamacita.'

On 28 November, as the judge at the trial in Spanish Town gave his verdict, the women interrupted. They were pregnant. Examined, it was found to be true. Both pregnant by Rackham, and they'd fought like that. They were taken back to cells, to be hung once their babies were born. Mary died of sepsis just after giving birth. There's no firm record of Anne, but she didn't die there.

For the seven or eight months they were in prison, they were held in cells so far apart, they couldn't see or hear each other.

✳

'There's one life.' Mary Read. 'I wanted the thrill of the skirmish. I wanted salty tang and sun on my skin, crystal sea, the creak of timber and billowing sails. Surprisingly, I'm a fool for sensuality.'

'And I wanted you.' Anne Bonny. 'Your attention.'

'Unfaltering, mutual respect.'

'Braveheart.'

Mary: 'Strong girl.'

Silence. A shared glance.

'I wish I was funny, though.'

'Anne, believe me, you can be.'

'Not like Jack.'

'Oh, he was funny.' Well, he was the death of them. 'Hilarious.'

They grip each other in a grinning handclasp. Oblivious to anyone else.

✳

An assured, very young woman becomes part of Ben's friend-
ship group. She's boisterous, pretty, Jewish, with an illustrious,
artistic family. Seems to have an entire house of her own in
Islington though I don't know how. She must be very clever.
Clever enough one day to have children that aren't entirely
stupid.

He doesn't volunteer it when he spends the night with her
but he's suddenly truly unavailable and when I ask, confirms
it. Allegedly she took the initiative. Looking at her, you just
know she would. Get what you want, you're entitled to it.

I lie on the bathroom floor of my flat and sob for hours.
My life seems to be one lesson after another in how not to do
things. Eventually I get up. I have two terrible terrible months,
when people seem embarrassed by my drawn face.

And then I realise I've begun to speak in my own voice
again.

✳

I refuse to sink.

What's the time? Right. Pull on my boots. Start walking
toward Maze Hill station then running, the theme from *Pirates
of the Caribbean* in my head, da-da DAH, da-da DAH. Hoist
the colours!

It's raining hard. And there's Steve, coming out of the
commuter crowd and looking piratical. So he's wearing aftershave? In ten years, he has never cheated. That I know of.
Could he be wearing that for me, the Pirate King?

'Kiss him!' roar Suzanne Valadon and Memphis Minnie,
and even Anne and Mary. 'You need a kiss and so does he.
Not every man is worthless. If you stumble on treasure when
you'd ceased to trust your judgement, recognise it. Seize it.
Don't let go.' And at the station, in a storm, I do.

18

This might hurt

Do you know the medicine you need?

How is a kiss so big of a deal? Because it's so intimate, if it's real. And because it's me, him and me, it goes wrong. I'm as tired of this inability to be close as you must be watching it. He doesn't expect what I'm doing, and he's taken by surprise.

'I'm kissing you!' Well, grazing the side of his lip, but who cares? I couldn't have sex anyway; after its years of joy and anguish my vagina will no longer countenance it, and now it can pretend it doesn't even know what 'rampant' means.

'So I see!' He laughs and hugs me, grateful for the effort. We're in people's way as they go through the barrier and, sucked in the vortex of everyone heading up the road, we get bumped along and I try to say something but someone steps on my heel. Steve reaches for my hand and holds it, which seems shocking, and then we're at the lights, and then we're home. Steve puts down his rucksack and the thing is, it's not just me that's got problems. He doesn't say, Let's try that again and sweep me into some huge snog. We have had good snogs. But not for a while. He opens his arms. 'Come on...' And I go and hug him. We stand looking over each other's shoulder, taking a moment for each other, touching however obscurely.

Later, stare at the bathroom mirror. I wouldn't kiss me either.

✳

In the kitchen he says gravely, 'Could you come and sit down?' He leads the way to our tiny back room. 'Something to tell you.'

230

Of course. Samina. That's why he didn't respond. Well, let's get it over.

'Lost my job.' He spreads his palms. 'Did my best. Thought I was doing well. They were getting me to do presentations, which is why I was turning into a perfumed, suited-up fuckwit, selling the firm's rubbish contracts. But they're losing money, and it's last in, first out. Samina tried to keep me there; we did long days, and we got results.'

He rubs his jaw. 'And I didn't want to tell you this because you worry enough and you shouldn't have to. And I know I've let you down on other things.'

He clears his throat and looks up, painfully jaunty. 'But I've got ideas. I've emailed Sean. Joined a couple of agencies last week just in case, no replies but it's early yet. Sainsbury's might need shelf-stackers, done it before.' He smiles like Rocky in the ring. 'Any other ideas gratefully accepted.'

Go over and give him the genuine hug he deserves. I'm surprised how hard he hugs me back. Then say, 'You're too good for it, but there's always cat-feeding.' Joking, but we both raise an eyebrow. He's helped in the past, at weekends.

'Could I do that?'

I don't want to say, a wombat could do it, because it takes a certain self-effacing skill, so I say, I don't see why not. Then I text Terry. And five minutes later, or at least once Steve's done his week's notice, we're in this up to our big stubby snouts.

※

My father and I are actually having reasonable telephone conversations. It could be because he's lonely, now Hurricane Deirdre is stashed in her luxury care facility, though I don't think so, he doesn't need people. But he's... pleasant. Perhaps Deirdre was a more pernicious influence than her crossword puzzles lead you to expect.

'Deirdre doesn't know me these days. I talk to her, I say,

Do you remember our trip to the Pyramids at Giza, darlin'? Doesn't reply. Chin down on her chest.'

'I'm sure she's listening to you.'

'D'ja think so?' Musingly. 'She sleeps, mostly. And she gets taken to the hospital a lot. The Sunrise Lodge staff are very good, they know what they're doing.'

They do. Deirdre is their cash cow, and they'll keep her hanging on long after the last shreds of dignity have evaporated. But Dad will always think anyone connected to the medical profession is a sun god, and worship them as the Incas bowed before Atahualpa. My mind flits back to when I was seventeen or eighteen, Dad mentioning something he thought was relevant that I should ask during a doctor's appointment. And I did. 'Um, my dad wondered...'

Doctor Lewes, who I'd later despise, smirked and murmured, 'A little knowledge...'

I felt embarrassed, the doctor implying my dad was stupid. Now I think, it isn't 'knowledge', Alexander Pope's phrase is 'A little learning is a dangerous thing', and he and you are patronising morons. Because of your little amount of learning, pal, my mother's dead.

But. There was probably a lot dad would have liked the chance to learn about. He taught himself from books he found during house clearances, most of them out of date, which explains a lot. About a year ago, when I'd made a flying visit with Steve, he asked me as we stood in their garden, 'What does betwaar mean, in English?'

I looked at him. '*Bête noire?*'

I don't know if he was asking me to make a point; surprisingly, I didn't even think of that at the time. He just seemed perplexed. 'Is it black beetle?'

I said, 'You know it's a person or a thing you don't like, the bane of your existence?'

He nodded.

'It's literally "black beast".'

'Ah, that's it.' He looked at the sky. 'I see.'

I watched him head back inside. Definitely not making a point? But he'd turned good-naturedly. 'Cup of tea? KitKat? No? Right you are.'

All this time he thought it was beetle. Which suits the idea better, so why isn't it?

'You were looking for flannelette, madame?' Esther Clayson waits. The woman who'd asked about a chemise continues chatting to her friends, but at last she considers the girl – bird-like, high cheekbones, eyes that in a certain social circle you'd consider intelligent but with a sassy look she dislikes.

'Excuse me?'

'A warm chemise.' Esther glances down, indicating her wares. 'But it's lately suggested flannelette may be inflammable near fires. So I've also brought out –'

'Inflammable?' The woman laughs. 'The word is "burnable". But you don't know what you're talking about, miss.'

Forcing her toe against the leg of her counter, Esther nods. 'I have, however, brought out a soft cotton in a flattering oatmeal shade which you might find...'

'Be quiet, I'll have the flannelette. Give me three in white.' She moves away, calling over her shoulder, 'On my husband's account.' And continues: 'That's the trouble with employing girls. An older woman, perhaps, in a lingerie department, but then you risk fuddy-duddy ideas. I may go back to a dress-maker...'

Learning something, a lot or a little. Can be dangerous if it pushes people's buttons. Esther is learning to be a doctor, but she has to pay to do that, which means convincing her bosses at Portland department store Lipman, Wolfe & Co that she's obsessed with hosiery. She had a job with the store before starting at the University of Oregon Medical Department – in fact now, in April 1891, when she's twenty-one, she's been working at one thing or another for almost fifteen years. Her savings ran out, so here she is. 'Another sixteen months,' she swears every morning, 'and I'm back to finish my last two terms. Come on, just do it. Get through it.'

Her classmates are racing ahead, but she's found a professor willing to teach her part-time, so on her lunch break she hurtles to his office to take notes for forty minutes. At night, she pores over textbooks. She's got eye strain. She bathes her streaming eyes and opens another book.

And she's grateful for the chance to make an income in these vast new sales emporiums, distracting herself by thinking of slicing her haughtier customers open for dissection – deep into the abdomen, forcefully up to the sternum. Her problem is the floorwalker, her immediate boss. She'd confided her physician hopes and he laughed. Someone from her background, he said, could never graduate.

But a certain mantra keeps her going, something she came up with as a dirty-faced tomboy. Esther was born on her father's ramshackle logging camp in Washington Territory. Initially a sailor, Edward had left England's Kent for the States, dragging his wife Annie to a life of worse hardship than she'd had at home. He ruled like an overlord, and one institution was that his five children work from the age of six, a financial necessity with the way Ed drank away cash. Esther, watching her mother toil, sewing shirts, layettes, burial shrouds for money, decided her own response would be a phrase she made up, 'constructive resistance'.

Which meant observing unfair power but while you endured it, taking subtle action to defeat it.

✳

It's not like Steve doesn't have experience of trying to earn, right from way back. He was a great little footballer at school and got scouted but just missed going professional; he still plays five-a-side.

Supposed to go to university like his siblings, all teachers and civil servants desperate to avoid their parents' money worries (his dad a navvy, his mum a nurse), at sixteen – head boy at Wood Green's St Thomas More, which looks like a remand centre – he left school because he was in a band on the brink of a deal. They split but I've seen his lyrics, seductive and poetic and yearning, a cross between Echo & the Bunnymen's dark rock drama and Television's intimate intensity. I found a tape during one of our moves, jammed it into the player. He hadn't wanted to sing but they pushed him to the front. His voice was unexpectedly deep, earth-shaking.

While in the band he was a warehouseman at Marks & Spencer, where he unloaded lorries and had a fling with a married woman. Was the older woman imprint made there? He says he thought I was his age when we met. Oh, please.

He got a job at Virgin Megastores, and was soon a buyer. This is when Virgin's staff were alternative, all rockers, punks, screwballs, nerds, in bands and writing screenplays. Steve and another leathered-up goth collected cash from the tills each night; they'd stand beside the young cashiers growling A-ha songs under their breath ('Touch me... Hold me...') as the girls' fingers trembled. Richard Branson liked to get staff into fancy dress for theme days, and Steve's mates remember him strolling for a drink at the Blue Posts on Berwick Street dressed as Robin Hood, green tights, quiver of arrows, staring down the traffic. I think that shows presence.

✳

Women around the logging town of Seabeck are dying in childbirth, haemorrhaging after miscarriages, enduring hellish stillbirths; while the men pretend the world is all about them, women comfort each other or find homes for motherless babies. But a young midwife, Annie Craig, moves here, and she doesn't just help with birth, she shows women, with barrier methods like early diaphragms, how not to get pregnant.

Edward Clayson goes crazy. Craig is 'a low hag... destroying the seed of mankind'. The Government and church speak out against contraception too. But as Kimberly Jensen writes in her book, *Oregon's Doctor to the World: Esther Pohl Lovejoy and a Life in Activism*, the handful of midwives initiating this are giving women some control of their bodies. *This* is constructive resistance.

Edward takes up farming, opens a hotel but falls repeatedly into debt and when his sons, now young men, refuse to follow his hopeless instructions, he roars at them to leave, so the family en masse do just that. 'Life without Father,' wrote Esther, 'was easy. We soon found work, and some of us sent ourselves to college, and none of us ever ran into debt.'

✳

Then Steve found a job he really wanted, and opened a small store with a couple of friends selling books about music, the only rock 'n' roll bookshop in the world. In Soho, which in the 1990s was still sleazy, so rents were cheap. They worked eight days a week and the place was a magnet, Robert Plant coming to browse, the Gallagher brothers, Prince in disguise. Bands played the basement studio; Steve and his co-manager

Conor started a publishing imprint and there were riotous launches. At Christmas, they put three singing teddy bears, sent by a fan in Cologne, in the window. Those bears were the stars of Denmark Street.

✳

Now in Portland, Esther still thought about midwife Annie Craig. She took a job at Lipman's dry goods store and might've stayed there, not knowing how to get further, if her mother hadn't invited a friend from Seabeck to dinner. California Brown was one of Portland's first licensed female doctors. At twenty-two, widowed with a small daughter, she'd taught by day and studied at night before getting into med school, where until recently women had been banned.

She loved her job, and could make $2,000 a year. 'For work you love,' thought Esther, 'instead of $300 a year for work you hate.' Callie advised her to try for the new University of Oregon Medical Department. In 1890, Esther got in.

It was two years before she could start because after the entrance exams, she had to save for tuition costs. The family, now all transport drivers or in retail, had no confidence in Esther becoming a doctor, it was too big. She nodded and carried on.

And finally, after making up her mid-course shortfall at assorted hosiery counters, she returned to college, the only lower-class person on the course, and qualified in 1894. At twenty-five, she was the second female to graduate from UOMD; she would've been the first but for taking those years off to work. With impressive marks, she applied for an internship but, as she later wrote, 'The possibility of a woman winning an internship had never occurred to anybody until that awful thing, my application, happened.' The professors met in consternation and emerged with a new rule; from today, women would not be eligible for intern posts.

237

19

So Steve was running his book emporium, starting his publishing imprint. What was I up to, so recently heartbroken? I took an audit. I hadn't written fiction for over two years. Hadn't even written a feature. I was a sub on a news mag. And it's okay if that's your goal, less good – and we've been here – if you tell yourself you do it to fund something else if you're too tired to actually *do* that something else.

And then I lost my contract due to budget cuts and was back scavenging for crumbs, single-handedly subbing the fiction pull-out for *Woman's Own*, where I struggled so much with the deadline I was going in free at weekends. That finished and, desperate to pay the mortgage, I got on to a scheme training people to go door-to-door at night with a Transport for London questionnaire.

I thought, hang on. I'm thirty-six. I sacrificed something important for that course and this is how I end up? What decent writing that I believe in could I pull off to make at least some income?

Broadsheets. Still, for me, quite thrilling. Forget fiction for now, it didn't pay and you need money. I'd always longed to rip a serious newspaper off a stand and see my name in it. The rock press was obsessed with how bands were interconnected, their musical influences, guitars, equipment. But I wanted to ask what emotions made musicians write the way they did, what moved them. 'That's women's magazine stuff,' said one rock mag editor. No, actually. I know there's another way.

And constructive resistance.

There wasn't much about music in broadsheets or their supplements then. Even less written by women; in fact there was one woman at the time, and seeing her name inspired me. So I sent arts editors my cuttings; ignored, I wrote again.

And it worked. Amazing where having no pride or shame can get you. On the third time of begging I got a live review for the *Independent*. The Go-Go's. I typed it up and posted it – 'You posted it?' screamed the arts editor. I got a fax machine and strong-armed them into letting me do interviews. I pounded away at the *Sunday Telegraph* until I found a gap and squeezed myself through it. I was interested in what kept musicians going. Was their music therapy, and a need? How hard did they have to try to get it right? What made love worthwhile for them, or wasn't it? Where did you have to put your mind to make life work out?

It wasn't easy chasing interviews and pinning them to the ground ahead of freelances on other papers. What made it worthwhile was the conversation with that musician. And the writing of it, later.

In New York, staying at the Paramount on deafening Times Square, where I had to put balls of rolled-up toilet tissue in my ears to even think. I'd been subbing the day before, got a night flight and was up at 5am, making coffee with my Argos travel kettle. Walking to the Upper West Side, welcomed by a doorman and into the elevator to meet Tony Bennett. Bennett talked about his wartime experiences, about Judy, Liza and Frank. I told him my dad had sung 'Stranger in Paradise' to my mum once in the kitchen – 'Take my hand, I'm a stranger in paradise, all lost in a wonderland...' and he grinned and nodded. He told me about seeing the music for 'I Left My Heart in San Francisco' and said, 'So I thought it might sound like this,' and sang me the opening lines. When I left, the sun glittered on Central Park. Bennett was optimistic. It was catching.

I spoke to Nick Cave, again and again, he must've thought he was trapped in a revolving door. Kylie Minogue said my

239

quads were too big and I shouldn't have cycled to the interview. She was tiny, tiny. I'm short but I felt like Schwarzenegger.

The papers I wrote for, mostly left-wing, did pay but quite little – £200 for a feature – so I was also still subbing. I got some overnight live reviews, a quick hit and ego buzz. After a day in an office fitting copy, at 6pm everyone would go home and I'd hang around. And at last pedal to wherever the gig was, Borderline or Town & Country or Kilburn National. Tense, because the review had to be phoned in by 11pm. José Feliciano at the Camden Jazz Cafe was delayed. At ten o'clock, Jose was lead onto the stage. He was good. I mean, he's really something. He did a lot in Spanish, he sang 'Light My Fire', and shortly after that I couldn't take it any more. In the toilets I locked the door, put the lid down, knelt on the wet toilet paper and bloody Tampax applicators and scribbled the review. Outside, I hunted (this is before mobiles) for an unvandalised payphone. Halfway down Parkway, a phone with the receiver still attached. Dial tone! Called the *Independent*'s copytakers and started dictating my review. Finger in one ear so I could hear myself I missed the first crash on the outside of the box, and turned to see some stoner trying to boot the door in. I waved my hand but they kept doing it. Copydesk woman said, 'What's that noise?'

'Just someone booting the door.' I opened it. 'Fuck off!' Cleared my throat. 'Full point, new paragraph. As the sax begins a logy refrain...'

Next morning at 6am I went round the newsagent's before work and bought the paper and deliriously told the Bengali owner, 'I've got a piece in this.' Riveting for her.

✳

'You're going round in circles. If you worked with a scalpel the patient would be half-dead, screaming for mercy.'

You did it yourself! Round and round, department store

after department store...

'No, I moved forward a step at a time, consolidating, not covering old ground.'

It was new ground to me. And I enjoyed it.

'What was the goal?'

Just enjoying it. Getting income from doing one thing I enjoyed. I tried to get a staff job writing. I couldn't.

'But if you wanted to do the other sort of writing, time was running out.'

If I hear that phrase again I'll go mad. I'm not superhuman. I got better at running several work streams at once but I guess no one will point to me and say, she makes it look easy.

'No.'

Thanks.

✷

If only it could have carried on like that. Even though, yes, I was doing the same same and no different to when I wrote for assorted music papers and subbed to subsidise it.

But two things happened, like they do. First, I placed an interview with Ike Turner. A chance to ask about his life with Tina and how he justified what he'd done. With my background it was something I couldn't pass up. But I looked at the time I had to turn it round, and realised that would be the next two days. Press week on *Just 17*. I could do the research that night after work, plan the piece before dawn, get to the interview in my lunch break if I pedalled fast. But I'd have to stay late to make up for that time. What about transcribing and writing it up? And then it hit me. I had eight hours all through the night when I could work instead of sleeping! I could finish and go straight in to the other job.

When your body's wired, cortisol shuts down digestive functions, sleep, immunity. I was ill half the time but filled with manic energy. So I did this piece and Ike was an idiot, so at least it wrote itself, and I went to bed for two hours and then

I went to work. And not long after I got a prolonged bout of pelvic inflammatory disease, where my temperature went through the roof and I had to run cold water on my wrists in the toilets. I was almost forty. You can't keep it up if you don't look after yourself. I'm not the only person to learn this.

And the other thing that happened is, the print world was changing. Computers meant you needed fewer staff, and subs' desks went from eight to four to occasionally nothing. I'd turned down full-time subbing jobs so I could write, but now I struggled to get shifts. Finally, I found production work on marketing magazines, where you're pleasing a client, and all the reps have agendas. I started lying my head off, encouraging people to get more credit cards, bigger TVs.

✳

Terry's come round with this week's keys. He knows Steve is joining in, seems fine with that. Steve listens to the roll call expressionless while I take notes.

'Jane and Mr Rochester, as usual. Mimi and Ferragamo, the Admiral and his bird are in Trinidad or somewhere. New one, Cronos, out by the riding stables in Charlton. The woman is crazy, don't touch anything. Nothing. She even measures the toilet roll, so take your own if you might need it. Dylan and Thomas, Persians, right at the end of Deptford High Street. Dylan has one of his tablets every day. Crush that up. Give it to him with two prawns, which you take out the freezer and run under the hot tap. Lily, watch out; she's a monster, I hate that cat.' The card he hands me says, in caps, VICIOUS CAT. 'Fleur in New Cross needs a tablet, not crushed. You'll have to get it down her. I can do it, you can do it...'

When he's gone, clear a space on the kitchen worktop and lay out cards and keys in order of how I'll pedal to them so the keys are sorted in my bag and I don't get in a muddle, plus I don't have to retrace my steps from one end of south-east London to the other. Steve watches. Then he says, 'Respect.'

*

Esther had to subsidise her dream with shop work, but her dream job would give her security and real income, that's the difference.

Her aim was to be a GP helping families like her own, specialising in obstetrics. In Portland at this time, birth usually happened at home, and most doctors were male. 'Throughout the long hours of a tedious labour,' Esther later wrote, 'the doctor usually dozed within hearing of the patient's bedroom and judged the progress of the case by the tone and tempo of her screams for help.' Obstetrics was the key to family practise and it was neglected.

She concentrated her efforts on the immigrant community of Little Russia, along Union Avenue. Patients weren't interested in a young girl who'd just set up, but one of her friends managed a telephone office and sometimes listened in on open party lines. She heard a frantic man trying to find a doctor for his wife, in labour, and called Esther with the address. Esther arrived, sterilised her forceps, delivered the baby, and her fame spread.

Soon, she could replace her bike with a car. She joined groups for the growing number of female doctors, gave lectures on health, and presented papers on subjects from abortion to difficult births.

But the Great Depression of the mid-1890s swept most of this away. In the summer of 1897, gold was discovered in the Klondike. Her husband Emil Pohl, another doctor, packed up and headed for Skagway in Alaska, a Wild West where they'd definitely need medics.

*

Esther Clayson now Pohl. What do we think she's actually like? I can't say because her newspaper pieces and biographical writings are, or seem, slightly posturing and smug. As if she stopped being the headstrong kid who ran wild in a logging camp, the Jo March tearaway, and turned into sanctimonious Meg. The trouble is, the biography I spoke about, *Oregon's Doctor to the World*, gives you little idea of the real woman. It's thorough, but it doesn't tell you what you need to know. Did she worry? Did she ever rest? She seems to have become so tough, almost... hard.

✳

So there goes Emil, the man she loves, to the brutality of the Klondike, and with him is Esther's beloved little brother Fred, now twenty-three. Fred sets up a provisions store, he builds the settlement's first new house: he is, Esther says, a trader, a miner and a visionary. Esther moves there too, to find a collection of frame buildings in a freezing world: that's her and Emil, in the picture a few pages back. Disease is rampant, but after a year she returns to Portland. Klondike life, even for the strong, was unbearable.

But Fred, the intrepid little brother? He vanishes on Christmas Day 1899, aged twenty-five, having travelled 196 miles on a bike on the Dawson trail back to Skagway. His body is found in the spring thaw, beaten to death for the money he carried. When Esther's son is born in 1901, she names him Freddie. More driven than ever and inspired by Fred's dedication, she becomes the first female director of the Portland Board of Health, and under her guidance school nurses appear, there is better sanitation, the milk supply is regulated to make it cleaner. Too late: Freddie dies at seven of septic peritonitis, a bowel ulcer thought to be caused by contaminated milk. He's buried beside his uncle at Portland's Lone Fir cemetery. Made of steel now, Esther's fight to clean up the dairy industry becomes a vicious, personal one.

The year after this she travels to Berlin for more training. She returns to hear that Emil, as committed as she is to improving people's lives, has died in Alaska in an encephalitis epidemic – inflammation of the brain.

A mountain of grief. She becomes armoured, and even more determined.

✳

Esther married again, Portland businessman George Lovejoy. His money helped her causes, but the marriage didn't last. That same year, she was pivotal in the campaign to give Oregon women the vote; taking over, in fact, from Abigail Scott Duniway. During World War I she worked in France with the American Red Cross, and continued to be instrumental in relief services worldwide – there's a bust of her in the town square in Nikea, in Piraeus, Greece, a mural in the Esther Pohl Lovejoy Hall at the Philippine Medical Women's Association in Manila.

And I still can't get a rounded picture. If I want to see her soft side, she won't show it. 'Don't expect tears,' I can imagine her saying. 'Don't hunt for fallibility. Those things weaken.' Making the bed one morning, it occurs: the problem's me. Why do I need her to pour out her heart? So I don't like her writing style. Maybe she's not smug, only confident.

And then unexpectedly, sitting on a train scrolling through the libraries of distant universities, I find what I'm looking for and nearly knock over my coffee. A hidden cache, a very few, of her most personal papers and journals. There's a letter to her younger sister Charlotte, typed with mistakes and tender urgency from Constantinople.

'There is a sound of revelry by night – Indeed there are different kinds of sounds of different kinds of revelry in different directions. I am on the upper floor of the Pera Palave Hotel. The room is rerectly opposite a winding alley and people are moving silentlt in and out of buildings on each side... At intervals weird strainsbof Turkish music and a sort of cgant floats down the alley and I cant make out where it comes from. I have been standing for perhaps ghalf an hour in the dark on this balcony...'

245

This is her. Here she is, at last. Among her things there's also a much-thumbed copy of the *Rubaiyat of Omar Khayyam*, and poems I can't read that she's written in her doctor's scrawl. She sees romance; *of course* she can still be touched, and deeply. There's a seam of emotion, an inner core where she kept the love with the hurt, and maybe her inability to relax, her need to fill every moment helped cover that with a protective shield. She cared too much, for everyone, so she concentrated to stay focused, keep bright. Constructive resistance on a grand scale; against fate.

✳

We've divided up the cats. At the end of Lily's gated estate near Deptford Bridge DLR, there's a stubby, dog-eared box of apartments. In the entrance hall the stink – rotten plaster, rubbish – hits me. The corridors upstairs stretch darkly. Open the flat's slab of a door. In a pitch black hallway no more than two feet by three feet, where the doors off are closed, a cat cringes against the wall. Her food bowls are in a shoe cupboard. Lily growls. She's not allowed out of this prison, only into the kitchen while I prep her food. Edge past her. The kitchen reeks. Pull on rubber gloves and start to clear the sink's dirty plates so I can clean her bowls. And so I can feel better. Lily trots into the shrunken sitting room, part of the kitchen, runs to the smeared plate glass window and stares out.

Put down her food, but she doesn't want it; just wants to look outside. Talk softly and she gazes at me, troubled. Don't touch, said Terry, and I won't. Sit on the hard modern sofa and read her card properly. This is the fourth time the owners have moved in a year. Lily is three. When they got her, she got pregnant. When they realised, they had her neutered mid-pregnancy and the embryonic kittens destroyed.

'Lily.' She puts her head on one side. This can be a bad sign, but it's not now. 'It's all right.' Although it isn't. Play with her for a bit, using string in my bag since she has no toys, and

246

once she gets the hang of it there's no stopping her. Make a bed from one of those fuckers' towels, and then reluctantly shut her into that tiny hallway again. She's watching me as I turn off the light and, wiping my nose on my jumper cuff, head downstairs to the sun. I've been there, Lily, in a place where there's no way out. Anyone would try to scratch and claw.

※

I was still hanging on at broadsheets. Jarvis Cocker, hilarious. Marianne Faithfull, gravelly and incandescent. I was also still subbing at marketing companies, though I was getting mouthy. 'How dare the client change this sentence to shit? Don't you care?' They'd look at me and shrug. What was I getting worked up about, I hadn't even written that line? 'Okay. Fine. Just let me do it then. And it's not even going to sell more for them, it's so much worse than the original. But isn't that why they employ journalists? To show them what a sentence is?' This might make me sound like a fuckwit but writing as well as possible, a good sentence, meant a lot to me.

I went out with a psychotic dean who lived in LA, which was interesting. Then another artist, excruciating. That theatrical lighting designer, a good man who wished I was six inches taller and blonde and got tired of accompanying me to review gigs and didn't read fiction because you couldn't prove it had happened. Despite which I nearly lost my heart, but I didn't. Early forties, I was only prepared for affairs from now on, cynical and beyond careful so no more random AIDS tests.

Then I got asked to go on BBC Radio Bristol to talk about upcoming music books. The manager of some rock book shop offered to drop off one that they had, about The Byrds. I was working at home that day, and answered the door in a paint-stained sweatshirt. A long-haired boy in black jeans, ripped leather and stubble handed me the Byrds biography. 'Good luck, it's a big bugger.' He had a Daniel Day-Lewis grin. I shoved hair into my pony tail and he leaned on the door frame. 'My folks live up the road, I nearly bought a flat here. Really like the vibe.'

I said, 'Yeah. Um...'

'We'd have been neighbours.' He looked at me to see how I'd like that, but I was a bit flustered. 'Well, seeya soon. Come into the store. And enjoy the talk.'

I was smiling as I climbed the stairs, and I said to my cat, 'Well, well...' I found out later Steve told his best female friend, 'I met the woman of my dreams today.'

✳

I fucked up the talk, though I think with practise I could do better. One Sunday months later, walking mid-bicker with the lighting designer in his pricey couture through Highbury Fields, I saw the boy – man – strolling with a friend toward me, deep in conversation. He grinned as he passed at my face of thunder, and I had a *Sliding Doors* moment – shouldn't I be walking that way, with that person? But the moment widened, we headed in different directions.

I went into his shop one lunchtime, just kinda browsing. He was behind the till, in a shirt with fraying cuffs because he ploughed the profit back into the business, watching me while I peered at the music magazines. We chatted and when I left, he said, 'We should go for a drink some time,' and the two hip girls who worked there considered me and I went very, very red.

He wrote to invite me to a launch, where he was behind the bar while I circulated. He appeared as I was leaving. 'Damn, couldn't get away, bar staff didn't show. How are you?'

'Have to go. Sorry.' I *was* sorry, too. I got up the circular staircase and as I bent to unlock Trigger he was there again.

'How about that drink?'

✳

We got to be friends. He was quiet, and I realise now that's because he was listening. He talked about his admiration for

Jane Austen's Elizabeth Bennett. I told him about the lighting designer, our ongoing ups and downs.

Me and the lighting guy had an awful mini break, him flirting with a tall blonde woman. Her tinkly giggle was 'feminine'.

We split up for the fourth time, only now he met someone else who wore designer, was all the things he wanted and from his own well-heeled Hertfordshire circle. I called Steve from outside work, and he said considerately, 'Don't look back.'

He told me later he'd been in a holding pattern, circling, hoping for this day.

We continued to be friends. We liked the same kinds of movies, talky and indie. We liked similar books. We went to see an arty short film on a steamy day in a pop-up cinema for two (yes, two) in Hoxton Square, and I was surprised, because he was so easy to get on with, at my thrill when they called out our names together. I thought, careful now.

One evening he made me dinner, then we went to a party on my estate, and during it we took a wander round the blocks and on a second-floor walkway he kissed me. He did it the way I should've kissed him at the station this week. I plunged in, feeling delight and a strange content, hanging on to his sinewy frame. Though I was never having a relationship again. Only flings.

✳

I don't have much time to write this lately. I sometimes scribble ideas while I sit with a cat before I head to the next one, but mostly I'm too drained. Frowning at that idea, head to the bathroom and find Esther Clayson there, going through my medicine cabinet. Esther was a beautiful young woman, but here she is in at least her nineties – she was still alive when I was born, died in 1967. She turns. 'There is enough oestrogen, enough progesterone in syringes here to help a woman who's struggling to get pregnant.'

Yes. I don't need the IVF meds any more but for some

stupid reason I keep them. There's pictures of the implanted embryos, too. Several pictures. Several times.

She sits creakily on the edge of the bath. 'Controlling fertility in a brand new way. Impressive.' She's still holding the packages. 'And did it make you happy?'

'No.'

'Because it failed?'

'Because it was made to fail.'

She looks at me, trembling slightly with age. 'But what can you do about that now? You're mourning in a way that I didn't, still going round in circles. Look at yourself.'

Glance at the mirror. I look older than her. Despite all my resolutions there's one thing I can't deal with and it's pulling me down.

'Aren't you actually *letting yourself* dry up?' And now I see sympathy. 'It's not intelligent.' She scrutinises one of the packets. 'I think you could do something with this.'

Try again, are you crazy?

'Try living again. With conviction.'

Yes. For certain reasons, my menopause has been refusing to come quietly. Night sweats, can't concentrate – I forget a sentence halfway through saying it, and I'm terrified it's dementia. But I was told to come off HRT, and I did.

'There's new thinking. Did your doctor quite grasp what had happened to you?'

Let me sink into being old. I've had it. Just let me give up.

'That won't work. And don't look back. Resist the things that happened constructively, by doing something about them. Look forward.'

At what?

'At whatever you put in the future.'

250

20

Dumbo

Take the risk

I'd been expecting Esther to hug me, but that's not who she is. Put down the toilet seat and sit on it. Is that what this actually *has* been about, finding a stand-in for Mum?

Well, you can't do that. Maybe you and your sister, like we try to, can be each other's mum. You can be your own mother in some ways or your own best friend. And sometimes, you can be a mother yourself.

You know I'd never yearned to be. Neither had my friends, but by the time I was forty a few of them had babies, and they were happy. I honestly never pictured it, in reality, for myself; the relentless grind.

But I was doing what I hadn't planned to and, fighting tooth and claw, began caring about this man. He encouraged me in my aims, didn't want to copy them or do them better. He understood my creative drive and, being from a council estate, the difficulty of affording it. He'd managed by doing two jobs to save a deposit on a crumbling studio conversion and was attempting to make it decent.

I began to remember what weekends were, and did things on them that weren't work. I'd come to believe I could only be healthily happy if I was working, only really be protected then: you needed to work hard to manage, of course, but also, even though work could go off and leave you, it usually didn't deliberately hurt you. Now I realised this wasn't as healthy as I'd thought. The things Steve and I were enjoying were such simple things, like strolling up the street early on Sunday to sit

251

at a sunny table in some still-empty coffee shop, or long walks, talking. Actually I was annoyed that Steve worked most Saturdays.

And then while I was beginning to have a life, section heads at two newspapers changed, bringing tame new stringers. I attacked different outlets but all had established freelances. I'd stopped living and breathing the job and was crashing back down the glass mountain. My only income option was to aim myself completely at marketing, and I wound up on the B&Q account writing about soft-close toilets, with a side hustle on the magazine for Tesco Baby Club.

✳

Steve and I have as usual split the cat roster but today, Saturday, I'm hoping we can have at least some sort of evening, especially as it's Guy Fawkes. We started early, heading out in opposite directions for the most far-flung addresses and working closer, and met at three in the afternoon to finish the tail end, so to speak.

We leave Jane and Mister Rochester for last, and after that go directly to the Dog & Bone one street away, all the keys securely zipped into the inside pouch of my bag. Usually I'd take the keys home, because if someone whipped my bag they would have the time of their lives – address cards, keys and alarm codes to every other house in SE10 and further. But I'll keep my eye on the bag, it won't leave my side.

The pub is packed. Edge myself onto a long seat at a vast stained table, Steve gets the drinks and, with my arm through my bag strap, we go over the day's highs and lows and co-ordinate tomorrow's visits.

As explosions gather pace, we have another drink. A fiddle band strike up. And though I thought I was tired, I drag Steve to his feet, and we dance, him with the backpack on, with the heavy load of keys inside it. You thought we were gonna lose it, didn't you? Instead we jive and bounce and strut and grab

252

each other's hands. This is the only touching we do, and it was rare until now. But we're promisingly good at it.

At the end, as we shrug on our coats, a group of twenty-somethings are leaving too. 'Great dancing,' says one of the girls.

'Tsk, aw...'

'Can we ask you a question? You two seem really into each other, the way you talk, the way you dance. We've got a bet on. Is this your first date?'

I look at the girl. Then I hug her. If only she knew the threads of what we have. But she's seen something, maybe. Has she?

I need to tell you briefly about Mabel Stark. There she is, close up and personal with her guy; other images show her lying in the big cat cage being stroked by a tiger, loving it, like Angela Carter might've done. In Carter, the beast is often gentler, more chivalrous than any man, and in her story *The Tiger's Bride*, the girl leaves behind her repressed human self; as they make love, the tiger's rasping tongue turns her to fur, and she becomes an animal too.

Looking over old Ringling Brothers and Barnum & Bailey

circus posters, you see illustrations of Mabel and her own significant other. 'Miss Mabel Stark, the Intrepid Lady Trainer Wrestling the Now Friendly and Willing Once Terror of the Jungle'.

Stark was the most famous female tiger trainer ever. Not that there were many.

Fully grown, a male tiger can weigh forty-eight stone and be almost thirteen feet long. Males have a wide forepaw pad, so you can see if there's been sex from trackmarks on the female's body. Tigers prefer to live solitary lives. They don't want to be messed with.

Mabel is just five foot tall. Sheikh could kill her. Rajah, her favourite, her love, could kill her. Love and death together.

Mabel played around with the facts of her life for a better story. She was born Mary Haynie around 1889 in Kentucky or Tennessee. She was an only child or one of seven, daughter of sharecroppers, and began to work the fields as a toddler. It was a miserable, isolated childhood. When she was eleven or thirteen or seventeen, her father died, followed by her mother – a woman who often beat her with a wooden butter-mould paddle, and who'd remarried. Mary didn't want to live with her stepfather, who she said was unkind. The problem with the rest of her life looks like it's somewhere in here.

She lived with an aunt, became a nurse in Louisville and hated it, then married, apparently. Nervous breakdown; because of that, he commits her to a mental institution, which a husband could do. She's sterilised there.

Within a year she's left the institution, left her husband, and is working as a carnival erotic dancer. One evening, strolling in Venice, California, she hears growling beyond the fence of the Al G Barnes circus. Wriggling through the gate she finds herself looking in the moonlight at a rippling, pacing Bengal.

She's captivated. She wants nothing but to work with these

beasts. Getting into the circus as a horse rider, she sticks like glue to head animal trainer Louis Roth, marries him, is coached by him. Roth uses revolutionary methods, promoting the unusual idea of encouraging the tigers to perform by rewarding them with meat instead of bludgeoning them into submission. Stark – a name she picks at random, stripped of femininity – challenges and communes with them. Roth is sacked for his alcoholism. Stark takes his place, eventually showing eighteen animals at once. Which would take a super-human level of concentration.

✳

I have my own cats to wrangle. Christmas is approaching, and that means forty visits a day. In mid-December, I start battling through a series of short marketing contracts on magazines for a bank, a mobile phone company, an estate agency chain – and through an increasingly heavy cold, wheezing and streaming with snot.

Each night, more cats have been added to the forthcoming yuletide roster. In the lull before the storm, Steve is shouldering the cat cross while I work. He gets in knackered from pedalling – it's quicker than driving on congested 'traffic-calmed' streets. We're up to fifty visits a day for Christmas now.

✳

How did Mabel get so good at this job? She was devoted. She said every man in her life but one was a marriage for professional reasons, as a step up or to obtain coaching.

Could she even love men? She never cared about a man the way she loved her tigers, and none of those came close to Rajah. She took him in as a sickly cub rejected by his mother, raising him by hand. As he grew, Mabel noticed how well he responded to touch, and although she said tigers could never be tamed, began training him to wrestle with her, something that hadn't been done. She was twenty-nine, with peroxided hair, and wore the tight uniform all lion tamers wore. She

255

planned an act where the audience thought she was being attacked. Men would come running to the edge of the ring, women screamed, reporters couldn't get enough of it, and her fame blazed. But of course Rajah wasn't hurting her. 'When I turned and called him, he would come up on his hind legs and put his feet around my neck. Pull me to the ground, grab me by the head, you know a male tiger grabs the female by the neck and holds her and growls till the critical moment is over... We kept rolling over till he was through.' She replaced her famous black leather bodysuits with white, which wouldn't show Rajah's semen.

Actually, it's not awful. Rajah is happy. Mabel loves him but she's a businesswoman. This is publicity, and it works.

She went on moving through men until she met Ringling Brothers menagerie boss Art Rooney. Rooney had shown no interest in women til now; he wore nail polish and looked female not male, which might be why she could care. She later said Rooney was the only man not threatened by her love of the cats. He died, and no one knows how. But how? Did Rajah, her pale-eyed, five hundred pound big cat rip him to shreds in a jealous rage? Did she let that happen, as Robert Hough suggests in his novel *The Final Confession of Mabel Stark* – throwing away the happiness she didn't trust before it could leave her?

✳

I'm so tense about Christmas that the cold settles down in me. Everything in my head and chest is pain and congested glue. Antibiotics don't seem to help.

Finish a series of interviews on the mobile phone magazine ahead of time and the Australian chief operating officer follows me into the loos. 'Okay, you're done. Pack your stuff.'

'But I was booked for another ten days. Honestly, I'm not infectious.'

'Tough. You're finished here.'

Leave as grubby snow begins to fall on SE1. Next day I've got bronchitis. For the awful Christmas that's looming.

✻

Mabel said she hoped she'd eventually be killed by the tigers; she certainly expected it. A year after Rooney's death, when she admitted that after losing him she could find no happiness other than with her cats, she was traded by the Ringlings to another, mid-sized circus. One torrential night in Bangor, Maine, the trailers pulled into the performance lot late. It was dark, cold, and in the cages the tigers roared in fury, having spent the day on wet bedding. Worse, there wasn't time to feed them before the show. This would normally mean the act was cancelled, but Mabel, then thirty-eight, went on – a decision, as Robert Hough has suggested, that might have been the first of her suicide attempts. Slipping on mud in the ring, she was gored grotesquely. She said in a newspaper interview, 'Sheik was right behind me and caught me in the left thigh, tearing a two-inch gash that cut through to the bone. I could feel blood pouring into my boots.' A second male, Zoo, leapt from his pedestal and jerked her to the ground. With his forefeet on her leg, he lowered his head and ripped.

It took 378 stitches to close her wounds. The deltoid muscle in one shoulder had been torn away, as was one breast; her scalp was virtually sliced off. She was back at work, against doctors' orders, in six weeks.

Stark was sold back and forth between circuses for years, winding up in a training job at a theme park, Jungleland in California's Thousand Oaks. In 1968, Jungleland was sold, and the new owners didn't enjoy seventy-nine-year-old Mabel's irascible personality. She was fired, left to pace her small home. And then she heard that Goldie, one of her tigers, had escaped from her exercise pen and been shot dead.

She thought about this for a day or so. And then she swallowed as many of the barbiturates she'd been given for

257

insomnia as she could and tied a dry cleaner's bag over her face. Her body was found on 20 April, 1968.

Years earlier, she'd said, 'If ever I can't have my tigers, it's sayonara, my friend.' She meant it. Mabel should've been born a tiger, and if this was an Angela Carter story she'd have become one. So let's tell ourselves she floated up, in a muscular tiger's body, from the crumpled frame her house-keeper discovered. For years, Kate Winslet wanted to make and star in a film about her. Because she was glamorous, professional and brave. Just not brave enough to remove the protective steel arena from around her heart.

✳

But I guess this is where things gather pace, because I'd tried to do that. We sold my flat, sold Steve's, and moved in together south of the river, where it was cheaper.

One of Steve's friends was a single mum. At a party she arrived and her little boy ran up to Steve and Steve lifted him and swung him around, and I discovered they had the same birthday and a special bond.

Not one man I'd been out with had wanted kids when it came to the crunch, or not with me. And Steve didn't. I said very tentatively, 'You realise I'm probably too old to have children?'

'Yup, not a problem at all.'

And I thought, that's fine. But he would be a lovely dad and I suspected one day he'd want to be. He'd stay with me. You see, I met this man and I didn't want children, I wanted a funny being made up of both of us or at least one of us that we could talk to and teach things and... I wanted to touch a baby and maybe feel – not that I'd brought back the ones I'd had to part with, but... well yes, maybe that I'd brought them back. But it wasn't just the past. It was the future.

We'd met when I was forty-two. Got together when I was forty-five. Spent time together, done up flats, moved. I was

258

almost forty-eight. Steve was hesitant for months until at Christmas in St Ives I sat on the stairs and sobbed and he said yes, we should at least try. I stopped using protection. Obviously nothing. Before I could stop myself I called a load of IVF clinics and found one that was happy to work with me and sounded kind. After our first appointment and a scan, we sat in a coffee shop and it was sunny and quiet like heaven in there, very early morning, and he took my hand and said, 'You were right. This is the best thing we've ever done.'

I was in good shape but they weren't going to use my eggs, so we became part of an egg-share scheme, two couples going through it at the same time but I'd pay the donor's IVF costs and be given any extra eggs she produced. It cost a lot of money. I took a deep breath and withdrew the first instalment from my savings, emergency savings for when I couldn't find work.

Maggie said, 'I'm really happy for you, but have you thought about this?'

I said, 'If I thought about it, I wouldn't do it.'

21

Thanksgiving Day 1875, and a dusky girl who looks like a native American stands in a Cincinnati field. She raises her rifle. The audience lining the ring is quiet. Phoebe Ann Moses was born fifteen years ago in Darke County, Ohio. Her father Jacob died of pneumonia when she was six, leaving Annie, her mother and her five siblings. The local Katniss Everdene, before she was seven she was hunting, shooting and trapping to support the family, trading game to shopkeepers who sold it to hotels in the city. When that didn't bring in enough, Annie was shipped off to work on the poor farm, and at nine 'bound out' to a local family to pump water, cook, and care for their baby. After two years of exhaustion and abuse she ran away. Taken in by various families, at fifteen she came back home, hunting more tenaciously, selling game to Ohio restaurants and hotels and paying off her mother's mortgage.

As the November wind picks up, she takes aim. Her rival Frank Butler, a tall, good-looking Irish immigrant, just smiles. She's a kid, and he's twenty-eight. What a sweet face she has. Utterly focused. But she won't – well, damn, she's hit it.

Travelling show marksman and former dog trainer Frank E Butler was touring with the Bauman & Butler shooting act, but he liked to offer challenges. He couldn't believe this girl appeared. An insult. Wiping perspiration on her gauntlet, she stepped back and let him take aim.

They kept shooting. Annie hit her twenty-fifth target, her arms aching but not badly. Frank raised his rifle. His finger moved on the trigger. He missed.

And that was it. Though publicly humiliated, Frank fell in love. A divorced father of two, he'd never been interested in anyone else, but this girl was his match. In fact, she was better. He had no competitive male ego, only admiration, love and concern. They were married within a year, and when Frank's male show partner fell ill, Annie stepped in and they never looked back. Unlike other girls on the circuit, none of them as good, who wore risqué razzle-dazzle, Annie preferred buckskins, her plaid shirt buttoned, a lone star at her throat. She'd happily blow kisses and woo an audience, but once silence descended, she was a pinpoint of concentration. After they joined Buffalo Bill's Wild West show, Butler left the spotlight to her, becoming her assistant and manager. She picked the name Oakley, which she liked, out of nowhere, though offstage was always Mrs Frank Butler. Although around this time, Lakota warrior Sitting Bull, impressed with her laconic self-control, adopted her and named her Watanya Cicilla: Little Sure Shot. She could hit dimes thrown into the air, split a playing card held on its edge at thirty paces. She shot with her dark hair rippling down her back, kept out of her eyes under a cowboy hat.

They gave money to charity. Made sure Annie's mother and Frank's daughters had more than enough. And they brought their dogs into the act. Their favourite was their constant companion Dave, who would sit very happily while Annie shot an apple off his head.

In 1922, the Butlers were involved in a bad automobile crash that left Annie with a brace on her leg. She recovered and still performed in her sixties, but was weakened. She died at sixty-six of pernicious anaemia in Greenville, Darke County, Ohio, and was cremated. Frank was seventy-nine, and he stopped eating. He died eighteen days later. It's rumoured that Oakley's ashes were put into one of her most prized trophies and laid next to Butler's body in his coffin. They were interred on Thanksgiving Day 1926.

✳

I can't stand it. I knew the story when I started writing this but looking at their faces, thinking of their love, his support of her in everything she did... It hurts. Why? Who would refuse that, if they ever found it? I'm so sick of being blocked, having Mabel's steel cage still locked around my heart. When I want to be able to give, like Annie. It doesn't cost anything, it's not even like it's only for the rich. This is something I could have.

✳

The clinic found a donor, a half-Maltese girl who apparently looked like a thirty-two-year-old me, had had long-term issues getting pregnant and preferred immediate private treatment to waiting for an NHS appointment. As we had our bodies prepped, never at the clinic together, I left cards for her, messages of heartfelt thanks. She and her husband didn't respond, and I understood that. 'It will be our baby,' Steve reassured me when I wasn't certain who this child would be. 'It will be growing inside you, it'll have your blood, it will hear your little stories that you tell it.' We got six eggs, fertilised with Steve's sperm, and when two embryos were put inside me, in a hushed room at the clinic, we were dazed, in another world.

Things didn't feel right. Two weeks later we did the test. It was positive, though the blue line was faint. Booked at the *Sunday Telegraph*, I realised I'd have to carry my folding bike up five flights of stairs because the lifts weren't working.

Next day, I started to bleed. I mopped myself gently with tissue, murmured, 'Please don't go.' Out in the noisy office I struggled to concentrate, and the chief sub gave me back the page I'd just done because what I'd written was useless. The following morning, a bright gush of blood like a flag. I told Steve, 'We're losing them.' '*No.*' He held me, and he was shaking. I was shocked to see tears.

I called the clinic to let them know, and asked about the donor. She was pregnant, overjoyed. So something good had come of this.

✳

Christmas is not much fun. We're up every day about four but, stuffed with bronchitis, I'm knackered before we start. People have turned their heating off so the houses are bitter and the water's cold, and only boiling a kettle can get the dried food off the bowls. Odin, Ronnie, Reggie, Jack the cat, Jane and Rochester, Twix, Teazel, Dickens who lives on the seventh floor of a council block with a security coded cage lift, Jason, Minnie and Morris, Yossarian, Macbeth, another Jack (who is dying and shits absolutely everywhere, poor thing, is skinny as a rake, and must be let out and waited for while puppy pads are put all over the tiles), Hector and Achilles, both obese and on diabetic medication which means steroid shots twelve hours apart, and getting the shot into their neck is never easy ('That's it, you've got him. Let's speak calmly. Do it now. It's all right, good Achilles. No, it's gone over the floor, you dick, it was in his fur, not his neck...'). And on and on... By Christmas Day I ache all over. 'Come on, love.' Steve strokes my shoulder. 'Gotta get up.' We're on the road in the dark, in a rented Zipcar, heading to George and Mildred in New Cross. By 8am people are surfacing, lights are on, a few runners. Around 11am I have a bagel with antibiotics. It starts to rain. Around 6pm, I sit at Biskit's holding him.

'We can't stay here all day. I know he's a lovely cat, but...'

263

'Just for one minute. He looks thinner.' Biskit turns his topaz eyes on me. His coat is slick, like it's wet. He's in the final stages of his life, not long now.

'We've still got...' Steve riffles the cards, ''bout seventeen to do, including injections.'

'I'm so tired.'

'I can do 'em on my own?' But that will take forever.

We're home late and I go to bed while Steve watches TV and eats a packet of mince pies. Listen to carols, try to breathe.

I don't like my life much at the moment. Think about stopping writing this completely, but it's all that's keeping me going.

✳

The bookshop was forced to close – Tin Pan Alley rents went sky-high – and Steve eventually found his bid-writing job through an old Virgin crony. A year had gone by. Then we tried again with the best embryos we still had. I was fifty, but success had happened with other women of that age. The clinic had no doubts. Blood tests showed the menopause was still some way off.

Embryo transfer; pregnancy test. It was positive. I still have that test, along with the scan of the implanted embryos.

I talked to them, told them about the world ('This is a streetlamp; this is a book; listen, that's your cat Flossie purring'), sang them songs. We had names, Hildy and Elwood. I didn't know how we'd manage if it happened. We weren't like other people in the Harley Street clinic's waiting room. I was mostly modelling second-hand and Steve had the usual threadbare jacket. It was all being paid for with my years of savings. We said if it did happen, we'd find a way.

And then I did a major interview with a New York marketing wonk which failed to record. An hour of talk: empty hiss. In a deserted office I closed the door, sat on the carpet, tried to slow my breathing, but my heart was pounding. The bleeding started in the evening. Lying on the bed with my feet higher than my head, I sang to them. Steve was playing football, and at 8pm I texted him and said to come back.

Huge contractions, and they swam away in a sea of blood. It was eight weeks, ten days from a first scan.

✳

I wasn't going to try again but I knew I would. It's like roulette, you're sure the next time will be the one that works. With no viable embryos left, the clinic found another donor, one of a gay couple; the woman didn't look at all like me but she worked with horses and loved animals. We booked time off for the transfer, since doctors told me women usually didn't work but rested for a week or so after it. Two weeks before the embryo transfer Steve's mum, who still barely spoke to me, went into hospital. A stent had worked loose, piercing the stomach wall. Though her MS was advanced, there was no choice but to operate. That week, I went to the clinic for down-regulation; an injection that switches off your hormones, freezes your periods (still regular) and your own ovulation cycle so you and the donor are synchronised. In your womb now, just crickets. After the jab, I paid for a whole new cycle, and the donor's cycle, and stepped outside. Savings almost gone.

The stomach operation came and went, all fine. Then two days before I should have started taking hormones to rev up my insides from nothing to off the scale, Una plummeted downhill. I went to the hospital. Steve's dad, thirteenth child of a Galway farming family, sat by her bed, cap crunched in his fist, hand on his walking stick.

She'd been given the last rites, and while I was there they did it again. Steve's siblings behaved like I was invisible, which is what they'd always done.

Steve had been sleeping in a chair or on the floor of her room, but he came home that night. He sat with me in the garden and, wiping tears of exhaustion, said, 'Don't try now, please. I can't stand another miscarriage.'

But I was... I was physically in suspended animation. I'd had a kind of chemical hysterectomy. And with no money and little time left, this was the last chance saloon. I wanted to scream, You're making a mistake, we'll never get over this. This could be your family now, *our* family. I said some of that. At which point his sister called him and said, 'We need you back here.' Ashen, he pulled on his coat. 'I don't want to talk about it.'

So many traps life pushes you into, where there's no decent way out. The clinic said they could freeze the embryos, though it would make the chances of success later lower, because freezing can sometimes cause damage. They hoped Steve would change his mind, and I said he wouldn't. They told me not to take the cocktail of booster drugs. My natural hormones would eventually kick in, and I'd return to normal.

In the hospital, the stone-faced siblings were in the canteen and I went up to see Una. Wired to drips, she looked at me; Steve was with a nurse, so it was just us. I sponged her forehead. This is someone's mother. This is what I'd have wanted to do if I'd seen my own mother at the end. I took a swab, soaked it in water and put it on her tongue. She lifted her hand and held mine, touching me voluntarily for the first time. Her hand was cold and I stroked it.

Steve had to leave sperm at the clinic on the way to her funeral in Ireland. Next day, I got a call at work from the embryologist. Four eggs had fertilised. I should be on hormones, I should be going for the transfer in two days. Even if I started the medication now, it would be too late. 'You definitely want me to freeze them?'

I said yes and went out into crowded, blurred Regent Street and stood in a doorway. I tried to ring Steve but the funeral was in such a remote location that there was no signal, or maybe they were still in the church. That night, at a company do in a West End pub, I drank and drank and on the way home I fell off my bike.

The thing is, by now I was fifty-one. My hormones tried to be the seventh cavalry but they couldn't make it, not after everything I'd done to my body. The down regulation picked them off as they came through the pass. Within three weeks, I was in a profound, irreversible menopause and looked like a sewer rat. One minute I was juicy, the next I was a crone. And this explains the list of issues I have now.

'Sometimes it's good to do what you're supposed to do when you're supposed to do it.' That's Greta Gerwig in the movie *Frances Ha*. But what if there was no way to do it at the right time? You have to try at the wrong one, and look what can happen.

22

The big blue

Leave the ground behind

'I hate your mother! I hate her!' At the clinic, where they were shocked at the crazed state of me, a compassionate doctor gave me a prescription for HRT, said I could still try. Would they just tell me *anything*? I'd felt young, though I wasn't. To go on now seemed not just blinkered and vain. Given my withered insides, it was wrong.

✳

'You wouldn't even talk it through with me.'

'I couldn't think. I was in extremis, I was out of my head.'

'You didn't tell your family, during all those hours sitting together by her bed through the night. You didn't let them know, ask what they had to say.'

'They're devout Catholics, what d'you think they'd say? But I've told you I could never talk to them. We're not close. I can only talk to you.'

I got up and walked away.

✳

We donated the embryos. I had no genetic link, so only Steve filled out the forms. He wrote more than I expected. 'If you're reading this, that means you've made it, and I'm so glad... Stuff about me. Well, if bad things happen, I try to stay optimistic. It's all you can do, it's the best thing to do... I love reading, I try to write. Avid cinema-goer. I'm a decent footballer... We wanted you desperately, didn't want to part with you, but something happened to us and after it we felt too old to give you the kind of life you should have.

But if you want to, please come and find us. We'll be waiting.'

I didn't cry, though he looked like he might. I hugged him but I also wanted to hit him.

He was right, though. If it had happened, Steve would be fifty-two when any child was ten. And I'd be sixty-one. I'd known that, but now I really knew it. I already felt sixty-one.

✳

Maggie said, 'I'm beyond sorry. But having a child doesn't always bring you together. It can pull you apart. It's like being tied to a small drunk person.'

✳

And I never did cry properly, because I felt the whole thing had been my selfish, last-ditch attempt to make up for the mess of my life. I just had a weight of sadness on me, muting things. I couldn't look at pregnant women, who were everywhere, or tiny babies or even toddlers, although they were all I saw. I suppose I'd come quite close to that life. I set my face and looked away. And then the pain began to abate, and eventually I was able to be kind and talk to people who happened to have babies, briefly anyway, and as I stared I must've seemed like some over-fond granny. And sometimes, if I was lucky, the baby screamed or threw up.

✳

Wake in the night. Almost Easter, usually my favourite time of year, though this one will be busy. We just seem to plough on, day after day, getting up, making coffee, resisting the urge to lie down on the kitchen floor and go straight back to sleep. I'm grinding my teeth so hard I've chipped one. I'm still trying to be positive, but the brightest light in my life remains what I'm writing here, and attempting to learn from other women who started out like me. They spur me on with their hopeful drive. It's when you stop hoping and wanting that it all collapses. What do I want now, what is left? Drift and doze, and in my dream I'm in our patch of garden. There in the dusk is a woman who looks like a Lakota, adopted by Sitting Bull.

'I found a good man,' she says, scanning for something to aim at. 'One who recognised any talent I had, and I had a lot. He gave me support, made me myself, my best self. We glowed.'

I know you did.

'Did we have children? We were too busy.' I know, I know. But it's Steve's fucking fault I'm in this state. He didn't see what he was throwing away. He put his mother first and she hardly acknowledged him, she barely seemed to care about him.

'Of course she cared about him. And she was dying. You of all people, with the thing about mothers?'

Open my eyes. I go over this again and again and I'm stuck, and that's shit. It's Jabba the Hutt in my head, Dad in my head. Forgive. Unfurl. It's past time for this self-wrecking, this other-people-wrecking, to be conquered.

✳

There are more cats than seems possible at Easter, and Terry's other helpers, who work only occasionally, are away. Again Steve takes the brunt of it. On my roster is a virtually feral cat in a rented house on the river. It's filthy inside – this is a rich couple whose parents subsidise their jobs, and they have three kids and a dog as well as their psycho feline. I haven't seen Zwingmann on this week's visits, and he's so un-predictable I'm relieved. The food's disappearing so I know he's in here somewhere. Wash his bowls in the kitchen, crowded with unwashed pots and empty Harvey Nichols bags, and put the bowls on the window ledge where Zwingmann likes to eat. Brace myself and approach the downstairs toilet, a semi-derelict room in what was clearly once a pristine mod-ern house. There's very little in the tray, but I clean up what there is and let myself out. It's spitting. Cycle into a headwind

270

to the job I leave until last because it's so complex. This involves pounding up Maze Hill away from the river, over the heath and dropping down into Lee High Road. It's not the best in terms of travel planning but I've always done this one and I said I'd carry on with it.

Brandram Road, past Billy Vee Sounds, left into Abernethy Road, fall off the bike and tie it to a streetlight. Five cats to muck out, plus a hen house. Several hens must not be disturbed as they are broody. They can be moody, too, I've found.

Feed Palmerston and Gladstone, on site and purring loudly. Then cut up celery and carrots from the freezer, tear strips of lettuce. Unlock the mesh screen door and head through the garden. Approach the hens with caution. I do love animals, but some alarm me. I want to love chickens. But the beady eyes. The beaks. Open the hen house door. There's a lot of fuss and clucking and long cawing chicken noises, a lot of wing action. The whitest has laid at least one egg. I'm supposed to get that. Step over the threshold, reach in gingerly and as I do, skid on a slick of chickenshit, fittingly, crash onto my arse and when I get up, see that three bundles of claws and wings and feathers are bowling in the breeze toward the bottom of the garden and the railway line. Begin toward them, remember the cage, turn back to see more chickens testing their freedom. For once, my mobile is in my pocket. As I lunge fruitlessly at a hen, I see one of the runaways has got through a hole in the tall wire fence. Why don't I just go with them? We can sit on the tracks together.

Steve can barely make out my predicament. But he gets it. 'On my way.'

I've got four loose chickens back in their pen by prodding them with branches when I see him on the path between the fence and the embankment. Two clumps of muddy white are sitting entangled in grass, but I can't get through the little hole in the fence to them, I've tried. With two strides Steve's up

271

there, gets a chicken under each arm and scrambles back down. They don't even think about beaking him, they seem stunned. 'Can you open the front door? I can't get them through that hole.' I tear back inside and run through the house. He's standing there, blood on one cheek ('It was an accident, she didn't mean it'). Several bystanders in Lee High Road are observing, and I wave.

'Can we come in?'

'Yes, yep.'

'Don't panic them, please.'

We struggle through the littered rooms, unlock the hen house, put the fuckers in. Lock it. There is a gentle clucking, as if that was good fun. Steve dusts off his hands. 'I should've been doing this place. If there's one thing spending every summer of your childhood on your granddad's farm in Galway is good for, it's herding chickens.'

Sink to my knees on the grass. My face is collapsing and I put my hands over it to hold it together. Tears leak between my fingers.

'Hey, hey. Come on now. They're back. Nothing's wrong, nothing to worry about.'

'There's always everything to worry about.' This isn't what I meant to say. I can hardly get my voice out.

'There isn't really. That's where you're wrong.' He bends then kneels beside me and tries to peel away a finger. 'Don't you think I could easily feel worried all the time?'

'No. You think you can cope with whatever crops up, you don't think you're crap.'

'Actually I do, frequently. But I'm not. We've both got problems, Christ knows, but you and me – we're brilliant.'

A deep sob shakes me this time, one real, wrenching sob.

'They couldn't have flown, you know, though they could've got run over, silly things. But the wings on these have been clipped.'

272

'Story of my life.'

'Don't be self-pitying and ridiculous.' He blots my face with a bit of tissue. 'You're heroic. I've never seen such heroism, such determination and genius.'

'For *what*?'

'For life. You go for it, you throw yourself into it. Like all these women, your heroines; courageous. But you never acknowledge what you've achieved, you've said as much. And there's another thing. You know the reason we don't have sex? Because you never let yourself have anything you might actually want.' I think someone said that before, but –

Look up at him. 'How dare you? What about the pregnancy, the IVF, I tried so hard, I wanted that.'

'And so did I.' He actually reaches for my hands again. 'Don't you know I think about it almost every day? I would've loved a chance to see you with a child.' He grins, shakes his head. 'I imagine it when I'm cooking, you'd both have been giggling, pointing at me while I made dinner. *Look at him, what's he doing now?*' He's staring down at my hands. 'One of the happiest moments of my life was at the clinic, you sitting on my lap about to go in for the embryo transfer, and that Take That song came on.' Corny chart song on the clinic radio. *You and me, we can ride on a star, if you stay with me, girl, we can rule the world...*

We kneel there, one or both of us crying, and then he says, 'I was wrong, I made the wrong decision. I've known it for years.'

Some lead weight inside me shifts. Only slightly but it's the first time. 'I knew you'd say that when it was too late.'

'Yes. I let you down. And I'm so sorry.'

I knew he'd say that too, he's said that part before, only now it's solid and true. So I can stop and seriously ask myself, who's to know if I could've kept the embryos in there this time? Yes, I'd felt young but no, I wasn't, not for what I was trying to do.

Steve leans close and carefully puts his arms around me. The breeze has dropped, it's quiet. 'What you thinking?' He sounds tense.

I'm thinking, Yes, for most people, having children might be the meaningful passion of their lives. And once you decide to try you become obsessed. I've made a disaster of that entire situation. Then I think, did Aphra Behn have children? Did Catherine Walters, Elsa Lanchester, Memphis Minnie and half the other women I'm learning about now? The issue must've crossed their minds, maybe there was regret or lost opportunity or no interest at all, but they were concentrating on something else, they put their sometimes limited resources into that, and it intoxicated them and by the way is why we remember them. And I didn't initially want kids, it was a relief when I realised not going down that route was an option. But I met Steve and hazy fantasies burst into being. Now I'm punishing him for it. Punishing us both, when something we'd come to hope might happen didn't work out.

And if it wasn't this, like he said, would there be another barrier to put in the way of being happy? Sometimes you don't have to pay to be. And you don't have to stay sad because it feels safe. It's no insurance against fate, no safer than happiness.

Lean back from his shoulder and look at him. Actually, what do I have to give? What am I giving now, and what have I given for the last few years? He gently brushes hair out of my eyes, and at long last I say, 'I love you,' and I mean it. And then, 'And *I'm* so sorry.' And I absolutely mean it. Those embryos were partly made of him, not me.

Hear a raucous clucking noise, long triumphant yodels and happy peeps and trills and either I've become aware of the chickens or they were holding their breath. Start laughing. Steve is laughing. 'Thankyou, ladies, thankyou.' He shifts and says, 'This is doing my knees in,' stands up, and pulls me up.

274

'So.' Quite jaggedly he clears his throat. 'Do you think you can be contented with me?'

'Oh yes.' It's dawning on me how many other things we can have. It's just that I hadn't let us.

'Thank God for that.' He dusts his knees and peers at me. Me, the bag of washing with every disease known to man. 'Because I'm pretty damned contented with you.'

Wipe my wet chin. 'Wasn't I your first sweetheart?'

It's that whore Bathsheba Everdine's line toward the end of *Far From the Madding Crowd*, one of Steve's favourite books. He nicknamed me Julie years ago because he thinks – wait – that I look like Julie Christie, as she was in the film. To this, best to say nothing. He's often played dashing Sergeant Troy for me, and now he does it again. 'Come, madam.' But he kisses me not like lying Troy but, far more excitingly, like Bathsheba's steadfast friend and truest lover, Gabriel Oak.

When I open my eyes, the sky is blue...

And into it, as we pedal to the next address, because Steve still has cats to do and we've got time to make up (years of it), zooms Raymonde de Laroche, almost vertically above my head. I've been thinking about her a lot. I always wanted to fly a plane, before I even went up in one, longed to take my feet

275

off the ground. When I got my job at the tiling factory I thought with my first two months' wages I'd 1) buy mum a washing machine and 2) start flying lessons. Both remained out of reach.

Okay. At the start, there were a few female pilots, a select few. Most with the money to pay instructors.

But this is not our girl. It's 1908, and Elise Deroche is kicking up her twenty-three-year-old heels on stage as a dancer, singer and comedienne. A sexy hoofer. Not what her parents hoped for. Her dad, a plumber who specialised in unblocking toilets, was pleased she'd been a sporty child, with an interest in cars and motorbikes. Perhaps she'd make a decent mechanic's wife. Alas. Elise grows up tall, beautiful, keen on art and longing bizarrely to be a balloonist. As a penniless Parisian, her nearest approach to art was to go on the stage, using the intrepidly camp 'Raymonde', her middle name, and adding an affected 'la'. At her feet one night is Léon Delagrange, who looks mole-like but is young, rich, and an artist. Soon he's the father of her child, André. He is also one of the first men in Europe to take up aviation.

With Delagrange, she visits the airfield in Châlons, ninety miles east of Paris, where her lover's friend, aviator Charles Voisin, is building planes with his older sibling Gabriel. According to outraged Gabriel ('my brother was entirely under her thumb...'), Charles is stricken by Laroche. The machines are terrifyingly dangerous. Airfix kits, hardly more than twigs with flimsy skin stretched over them. Gabriel's bitterness makes the story more dramatic, implying as he does that Elise is a headstrong fool, and word gets out that she climbs into a plane that day. The Voisin was a single-seater, so the pupil sat alone in it, taking direction from a trainer shouting orders from the ground.

'Up you go.' Looking very like Kate Bush and shoving away her flowing skirt, the girl puts a gloved hand in Voisin's and grips the plane wing. Hoists herself, light as a feather, and clambers to the seat. Starts the machine and it begins to move. She gasps, grins, heart racing. No fear at all. Remember she knows about automobiles, understands engines. She taxies across the airfield. A mechanic turns the plane, and she heads back to the starting point.

She is not, under any circumstances, to take off. You don't say? Handling the controls with 'cool, quick precision', she opens the throttle, races down the airstrip and rises fifteen feet. I can hear her wild shout of triumph from here. According to *Flight* magazine's Harry Harper, writing at the time, the plane 'skimmed through the air for a few hundred yards, and then settled gently and came taxiing back'.

But Laroche is a mother and she's not a fool, of course she didn't do this the moment she saw a cockpit. She'd been taking lessons – probably free because Voisin is led by desire and she uses those huge eyes – for at least a week. Harry Harper was there for her second flight too. She circled the flying field twice, 'the turnings being made with consummate ease. During this flight of about four miles there was a strong gusty wind blowing, but after the first two turnings the Baroness said that it did not bother her, as she had the machine completely under control'.

Harry is certain a woman like this must somehow be nobility. She's a baroness, did I hear? Well, obviously Laroche loves that. No toilets in my background. Only stately homes, *chéri*.

Headwinds just make it more fun. Elise has the machine of life fully under control.

✳

Last day of the Easter break. I have been utterly conscientious, apart from the issue with the hens. I approach each front door knowing the alarm code. I gain entry, using gloves in my palm to cushion the pain of the awkward twist. Close the door

277

calmly, although there may be a shrieking automatic serenade. I key in the code, and if the alarm vaults up a notch I reset and do it again. Once they're fed I sit with the cats, or play with them, racing up and down the stairs with catnip-filled mice and tinkly plastic balls. Now the weather is better I am required to water gardens, traipsing in and out with watering cans. It's a lonely job, in fact. In some houses I pick up the book I started weeks ago and carry on where I left off, but there's only time for a page or two before I have to go.

When I work together with Steve, it's nicer. Sometimes. And sometimes now it hurts. On an estate on the way to Rotherhithe, drag myself up the smelly stairs behind him. Inside, he bends down to chuck three huge Maine Coons under their chins, then he rolls up his sleeves and gets stuck in to the tray, which is too small for them, as is this flat; cleaning like I've never seen him clean, putting in new cat litter, shaking the powder deodorizer, sweeping and often washing the floor. In a luxury flat in New Cross he does it all again, then sits on the sofa with Homer, the audacious ginger kitten. Homer adores Steve, and it's mutual. Homer twists around Steve's shoulders, rubs his cheeks along his arm, tries to get up his sleeve.

We're barely making enough to buy our groceries.

This final day of Easter, there's a call on Steve's mobile from Terry. Because he's up to his elbows in Country Hunter, I answer it. 'Steve there? Well, tell him I'm so fucking pissed off I can hardly speak.' If only. 'But Terry-'

'I don't wanna talk to you. I dunno what you two've been doing this week but it ain't good enough. I've 'ad a call from Muriel's owner. Had to park up and listen, and then I 'ad ter sit there trying not to come over and deck Steve.'

My heart is thumping. Muriel is the cat Steve was with when I was in Lee. When I needed help with runaway chickens.

'She's back from Sardinia and looked through her camera

278

footage and timed his visits. And on one occasion he was there for seven minutes. Seven. Fuck's sake. You are supposed to be in the house with the cat for twenty minutes. More, fine, if you got time. But seven is shit.'

'But sometimes there isn't time, Terry – '

'You make time. You start earlier. I ain't gonna argue, I'm coming over tonight.'

And he does. He hammers on the front door, scarier than the menacing tap. He walks in, drags out a chair. Accuses us of untidiness, skimping. He looks at me. 'Didja not wonder where Zwingmann was, eh, all week? I'll tell you where he was. Sitting under the bed upstairs shitting. Sitting *on* the bed upstairs, pissing. I got in there to check today and it reeked.'

He turns to Steve. 'But you. Leaving that house early, one time thirteen minutes early. To say I'm unimpressed would be an understatement.'

Steve says quietly, 'On three occasions Muriel, who is elderly, was asleep. What should I do, wake her up to play with her?'

'Don't gimme that. I've had to give them the money back. I won't see 'em again. Not after your handiwork.'

Head low, shoulders slumped, Steve's focused on the carpet. When Terry's left, I go over and hug him. He shrugs, grins. 'He's ridiculous. He does all that himself, and worse.'

It's true, but Terry is in the boss position. He's stressed, we're punchbags, and Steve who's worth a hundred of him is hurt and I can see it.

A huge roll of furious thunder, a simmering rage I've smothered for decades, begins in me. 'This is *fucked*.'

'Yup.'

'And that's *enough*.' What have I, what have both of us been through, what have these women helped me see? I'm mad as hell, and here's where I stop taking someone else's garbage. 'Show's over.'

279

Steve looks up. 'But I thought you wanted to make a go of it.'
'Me? I hate it.'

He stands, puts his palms on my shoulders. 'Good. I love the cats, but I do too.'

✳

Elise has captured Voisin's heart and mind. But he can't stop her getting into bloody planes. Ten weeks after her first flight she crashes, the tail of her machine brushing a tree. Concussion and a broken collarbone. The following month, she travels with the Voisins to Egypt for the Heliopolis air meet, and takes part despite heavy rain and winds. In 1910 she's the first woman to get a pilot's license, international license number 36. By now the press are calling her *la femme oiseau*, the bird woman. How's she affording all this? Well, her son's wealthy father pays for him, she herself is under Voisin's metal wing, and she still does stage work.

The peril she's in remains extraordinary. Other pilots are paralysed or they die, many from failure of their engine or the butterfly-like craft. At Reims, she stalls. Silence, then her contraption plunges. She's dragged from the wreckage and can barely move for two years but she works at it, forcing herself, limping, and improves.

A working-class girl, and I'm going to say it, who gets above herself, far above. Bumpy. Catastrophes, tumbling. It's hard but so much more than worth it. Higher than the clouds, flying and free. Wouldn't you pay any price? I would. Even just to have tried, to have seen it and felt it. Watching the dials, at peace in the place you should be.

✳

There had been a break in contact with Charles but now she's recovered, she pays him a visit. They're thirty, beautiful, dedicated. I can't find out exactly what happened, if they spent the day together, if they'd already spent weeks: walking, talking. I want to think 26 September 1912 had been a good day. They drink a little, laugh, and whether or not you were anticipating this, that evening their car collides with another near Belleville-Sur-Saône. Voisin is killed outright. In a car, on the road.

Grief; but a determination to fly even more, to imprint her truest companion and fellow trailblazer on the sky. During the Great War she offers to fly, is told women can't be relied on, and instead volunteers as a driver, chauffeuring French officers to and from the front lines, often under fire. Surviving this she wonders if she's charmed and, at the war's end, applies to train as a test pilot. There she is, in her bulky skirt, trademark white sweater and cloche hat. Navigating round obstacles, past bad luck, managing long-term physical damage. Flying higher, faster, further.

In 1919, she's accepted to test planes at Le Crotoy airfield. Regular income, so she and her son would never have to worry financially. She'll start as a co-pilot, learning from a man. On 19 July, a hot day, she lowers herself into the rear seat of an untried Caudron, a single-engine biplane, smoothing down her gloves, strapping herself in. Smacks the side of the plane and the pilot taxies and lifts. On the return landing approach, having handed her fate to someone else, she feels the vehicle lurch into a tailspin and understands she's going to die.

So Elise didn't live that long. She died, but we all do. She said, 'Flying is the best possible thing for women,' and she meant it. If she saw me now, what would she say? First, never surrender the controls of your plane. And second (how many people have to tell me this?), don't look back, don't keep looking behind you, because that's not the way you're going. Retracing my path to here has been very useful, but its work is done.

This is the last time I need to hear it. Only an idiot lives in the past.

✳

It's six months since that scene with Terry. I'm sitting on a grassy dune, skimming flat stones into a wide Kent bay. This is our home now. I've got a few cats I feed and dogs I babysit, I do bits of freelance scrawling and occasional shifts in London, and I've applied to join a local gardening team. It all pulls in just enough, so I've been able to go on with that thing. This thing. I've written quite a bit, I see, about tarts and pirates and painters and medicine women.

I've been feeling the years slipping off me. It's partly the relief, and also partly, I suspect, the new HRT. Esther Lovejoy was right: the research, carried out mainly by men, that stopped GPs prescribing HRT and deprived women for years was found to be sensationalist. I've got a progressive doctor here, he's as annoyed with those researchers as I am. Not everybody needs it but now I don't feel so exhausted, my brain's not lost, honking for help, in fog, and the most female parts of me feel listened to. I'd forced them through so many hoops, and they needed more support than they were getting. There's still no way I wouldn't have taken the most significant of those risks.

Catch a movement and turn to see, in the distance, a figure walking toward me. In cut-offs and a faded shirt, it's Steve arriving from his job managing a hippiefied wholefood store. He's owning it, vamping his retail experience by playing Bob Dylan and The MC5 and getting in a Gaggia. We still have rows, though about more interesting subjects, but we talk things over. We're both learning.

I'd hoped for a wild sex scene at the end for you, and for us, but it couldn't be arranged. We have, though, had a shag. What about that? It wasn't easy, with my contemplative vagina, but we took our time, Steve saying gently, 'No rush.' Which no man's said to me and it broke my heart, after so many years of accommodating assorted dicks. And I felt something I hadn't felt before. It wasn't solely focused on my orgasm and seemed to touch more of me than I'd expected. Could it be a balanced, tender, surprisingly provocative... real love?

So, how we came to be here. It was time to take control and be my own Wonder Woman: golden wristbands, neon lasso. The home I'd crippled myself to pay for was my gift from my younger self, the only thing I had left, and I needed it now and so did Steve, whose own flat's collateral had gone into our joint place too. We had to break our clanking chains. I bought a postcard in Greece years ago and found it again in the move, with its quote from Pericles. *The secret to happiness is freedom... and the secret to freedom is courage.* I needed space to breathe. Space to look ahead.

We sold up. Goodbye, Dog & Bone and everyone we know. Paid off the mortgage, got a tiny coastal flat, put the rest in an account that's our minimalist retirement seedling. Not sailing into the sunset, but the sunrise. I've got even less in terms of things. But, y'know, more.

That's when I realised that, like these women, I'm a ducker and diver. Used to having to think and plan, artful dodger, wheeler-dealer. I've never assumed things will be in place, and I take chances because I know somehow I'll come up with a way past the jaws of most disasters. Or anyway, through and out the other side. Me and my history girls are mutts, survivors. Sure, their lives and successes were often bittersweet; that just makes what they did shine brighter.

But they had one last lesson for me. If you don't have a dream, well, you can't easily have one come true – but like the wisest members of my squad, it's good to pan back and see the whole picture. Loosen up, not fixate on one spot, and even assume some things might go right on their own. Because they do, more than I thought, maybe just in ways you didn't expect.

You don't always have to work really hard, sometimes you just have to work things out.

I focus properly on Steve, a breakwater away. He raises a hand and, with the cat-calls and shouts of encouragement of seventeen raucous legends in my ears, then fading til they've vanished, I get up, walk to him and touch his face.

He smiles. 'How's it gone today?'

Instead of saying rubbish, say, maybe not too bad. Kick off my sandals. 'Shall we?'

'What, like this?' He shrugs, drops the backpack, pulls off his sneakers and shirt and together we hobble, stumbling on pebbles, the few steps to the glittering sea. Execute a shimmy when I get there, like when I'm drunk in the kitchen, and kick a ribbon of seaweed off an ankle. 'Dancing barefoot suits you,' he says. 'Patti Smith but better. Pretty much like some heroine.'

We advance and dive then, embracing the chill, me in my knickers and T-shirt. Splash back up, scissor my legs and send spray over my head. Sunlight flickers and bobs all around us. Man, it's beautiful.

I'm out of my depth again, and going further.

Acknowledgements

Emma Yandle and Dr Kim Simpson allowed use of their image of Eliza Haywood on p.113. The artwork was for *Naming, Shaming, Reclaiming: The 'Incomparable' Eliza Haywood*, an exhibition At Chawton House, Hampshire, UK, 20 March-4 June 2017 (I wish I'd known about this!). Courtesy Chawton House.

The image of Abigail Scott Duniway on p.125 is courtesy of the Albany Regional Museum, Albany, Oregon.

The image of Esther Pohl Lovejoy and her husband on p.233 is courtesy of Oregon Health & Science University Historical Collections & Archives, where there is much more about Esther.

Finally, the image of Annie Oakley on p.260 comes courtesy of the Buffalo Bill Center of the West in Cody, Wyoming.

Every effort has been made to contact all copyright holders. The publishers will be happy to make good in future editions any errors or omissions brought to their attention

The author back in the rock press days
when she wrote under the pen name
Carmen Keats

Ignite Books is a small, independent publisher. This book is the latest in our series which we hope puts fresh, thought-provoking, entertaining writing before a new audience. We have a lot of fun doing this, but we also survive on a shoestring budget and a lot of graft. So, if you've enjoyed this book, please tell your friends about us.

You can also find us on Twitter, so drop by and say hello. And to learn more about what we do, or shop for our other publications, just visit our website at ignitebooks.co.uk

Thank you.

Independent bookshops are wonders. Each and every one run by people passionate about books and the reading of them. Please support them when you buy, and help keep your high street thriving. Pop in and visit them, or do it from the comfort of your own home via either of these websites:

www.bookshop.org
www.hive.co.uk